Mills on t

A gazetteer of water-powered sites on the
Teign and the Bovey and their tributaries

Martin Bodman

Leat Press

First published in 2015 by Leat Press
25 Chaffinch Drive, Cullompton, Exeter EX15 1UJ

ISBN 978-0-9548758-3-1
British Library Cataloguing-in-Publication Data.
A catalogue record for this book is available from the British Library

Printed by Short Run Press, 25 Bittern Road, Sowton, Exeter EX2 7LW

Sales and distribution by
Tor Mark, United Downs Industrial Estate, St Day, Redruth, Cornwall, TR16 5HY

Contents

Front cover illustrations
Main image – The Teign in Dunsford Wood
Insets – Sowton Mill, Dunsford and the waterwheel at Sandy
Park, Chagford

Back cover illustrations
Images from top to bottom –
Mill leat, Yeo Mill, Chagford; Holy Street Mill, Chagford;
Mill race, Foxworthy Mill, Lustleigh

Acknowledgements

I am particularly grateful to Alan Stoyel, who has allowed me to digitise photographs of sites from his extensive collection, some taken in the 1960s before mills were demolished or converted.

Tom Greeves has very kindly advised on blowing houses, stamping mills and other sites on the upper reaches of the rivers. A notebook in his possession has proved particularly useful. W. H. Worth – not to be confused with R. Hansford Worth – was an engineer who visited working mills in 1926 and again in 1934, assessing water flows and water power in connection with the planned reservoir at Fernworthy. From it I have gleaned information on waterwheels and turbines.

Michael Moss and Martin Watts have also made substantial contributions to this volume, for which I am most appreciative.

I also wish to thank the following from whom I have received help in preparing the gazetteer:

Jim Black, Bovey Tracey
Les Breney, Bovey Tracey
Tony Brooks
Thomas Cadbury, RAMM, Exeter
Maggie Clark, Throwleigh
Steve Coombes, Chudleigh
Chris Elliot, WRE Ltd, Ponsworthy
Jon Evans, Manaton
David French, Stokeinteignhead
Derek Greenaway, Manaton
Bill Hardiman, Moretonhampstead
Abi Higgins, Christow
Tony Jewell, Kelly Mine
Chris Kelland
Lilly Mckelvie, Drewsteignton
John Madin, RAMM, Exeter
Geoff Morgan, Lustleigh
Judy Moss, Chagford
Brian Murless
John Pidgeon, Bovey Tracey
Karen Stevenson, Lustleigh
Pat Watson, Widecombe
Peter Watson, South Zeal
Alan Wesson, Sticklepath
Alan Wright, South Tawton
Margaret Wright, Bovey Tracey

At the Devon Heritage Centre:
Deborah Phillips, Ian Ponsford, Tony Rouse, James Ward, Jan Wood and colleagues.

Images on pages 9, 10, 18, 30, 33, 41, 65, 78, 79, 120 and 121 and are reproduced with the kind permission of Devon Heritage Services.

Please note that the sites referred to in this volume are on private property and there is no right of access. Some have vanished from the landscape; many more are house conversions. Anyone seeking access to these sites should apply for permission in advance to the respective owners. A number of sites can be seen from a nearby road, or from a public footpath.

Preface

This is a gazetteer of water-powered sites in the Teign and Bovey valleys in Devon.

Mill sites on Teign tributaries running through Newton Abbot, Kingsteignton, Bishopsteignton and Combeinteignhead to the Teign estuary get a mention at the end of the gazetteer.

The rivers Teign and Bovey and the Liverton Brook provide 125 sites, the focus of this volume. A further 48 sites have been identified in the rest of the Teign catchment, giving a total of 173: a considerable number. However, I cannot claim to have found all the water-powered sites in the Teign and Bovey valleys. There may be farm mill sites hidden away, waiting to be discovered.

For example, Smithcott in Bridford parish looks a possibility. Farms here were to let in 1815: *'.. A thrashing-machine, of the best construction, has lately been erected, and the estate contains two most valuable streams of water ..'* [Exeter Flying Post 15 June 1815 p 2 col 4]

This is a notice which suggests the machine may have been water powered. The potential site may now be under the Kennick Reservoir.

Much of the information for the gazetteer has been compiled over time, but recently I have been greatly aided by the advent of the on-line British Newspaper Archive.

This volume covers new ground. Inevitably with such material there will be errors and I can only apologise where these occur.

It is fortunate that most of Reverend Swete's watercolours of mills made in the last decade of the eighteenth century have been preserved at the Devon Heritage Centre. These give an indication of earlier structures at several sites.

Throughout the gazetteer I have adopted the term 'grain mill' here rather than 'corn mill' or 'flour mill', as the more inclusive concept. The word 'corn' is today often associated with sweet corn or maize. In grinding wheat, barley or oats a mill produced 'meal' which required further processing before becoming flour. By the end of the nineteenth century country mills had largely ceased flour milling and were being used mainly for animal feeds.

I have assumed some prior knowledge of how a watermill works. *Corn Milling* by Martin Watts is a useful guide to the operation of a water-powered grain mill. Maps have been redrawn from the Ordnance Survey originals to provide greater clarity for watercourses – the rivers and the mill leats.

Introduction

The river Teign

The Teign's source is at Teign Head on Dartmoor. The river, here known as the North Teign, flows off the moorland by Scorhill Down and runs east-north-east to Leigh Bridge, where it meets the South Teign which has flowed northwards from Fernworthy. Beyond Chagford the river enters a steep-sided and wooded valley below Castle Drogo, emerging into more open country at Steps Bridge, Dunsford.

Above Sowton Mill it turns roughly south-south-east and is joined by streams from Bridford, Christow, Doddiscombsleigh, Ashton, Trusham and Hennock. The B3193 road runs close by for much of its course, which is largely hidden in summer, under a canopy of trees. By Chudleigh it is joined by the Kate Brook which rises near Exeter Racecourse on Haldon. The Teign then glides south past Chudleigh Knighton to its confluence with the Bovey and on to the outskirts of Newton Abbot, where it enters a tidal estuary, finally reaching the sea at Teignmouth. It is about 35 miles (56km) long.

The river Bovey

The river rises on Dartmoor near Bennett's Cross and the Warren House Inn on the Moreton-Postbridge road. It flows north and then below Meldon Hill is met by a second stream which wells up at East Bovey Head near Challacombe Cross. Past Batworthy the river then swings around to the south east, passing North Bovey and on to the narrow wooded gorge at Lustleigh Cleave, between Manaton and Lustleigh. In Hisley Wood it is joined by the Becka Brook, which has dropped 350 yards (320 metres) in its six-mile (9.6km) course from Holwell Down. After the

town of Bovey Tracey the Bovey joins the Teign roughly a mile (1.6km) south of Chudleigh Knighton. It is about 16 miles long (25.6km).

Sites

The Teign and its tributaries can claim at least 80 water-powered sites with a further 38 on the Bovey and seven or more on the Liverton Brook.

Mills

On the lower reaches of the Teign waterwheels were often undershot or low breastshot, worked by the force of the water. On smaller streams and on the higher reaches of the Teign and the Bovey the overshot waterwheel and launder were commonly adopted. Topography influenced the type of waterwheel adopted.

A typical image of a watermill today is of one with a single external overshot waterwheel and many Teign mills fit this stereotype. But there

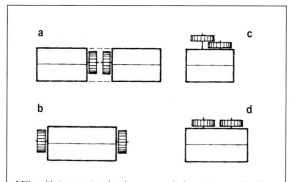

Mills with two waterwheels – example layouts seen in plan.
a = two internal waterwheels driving separate sets of machinery; **b** = two external waterwheels on end walls; **c** = two external undershot or breastshot waterwheels en echelon, requiring separate water channels. In all cases by-pass channels not shown; **d** = two external overshot waterwheels fed by a launder (not shown).
From: Martin Watts, The Archaeology of Mills and Milling

The Teign river basin
The gazetteer covers water-powered sites on the Teign above its confluence with the Bovey, as well as sites on the Bovey and the Liverton Brook. Mills on the Lemon and at other sites around Newton Abbot, Kingsteignton and Stokeinteignhead are listed in on pages 117–123

were also a number of grain mills where the waterwheel – or wheels – was internal: for instance Bridford Mills, Dunsford Mills, the woollen factories at Chagford on the Teign, Palace Mill, Chudleigh and Rushford Mill, Chagford. At Weir Mill, Drewsteignton, an external undershot or low breastshot wheel was installed at each end of the small building.

Another favoured combination of wheels in the south west was two overshots in line. The vanished Chudleigh Bridge Mill and Batworthy Mill, Chagford both had this layout as did Tawton Mills; New Mill, North Bovey may also have adopted it.

A typical country grain mill would usually operate with two pairs of stones. Sandy Park Mill ran with three pairs of stones. Larger mills, had more – Town Mill, Chudleigh had four and Dunsford Mills had six pairs of millstones.

Mines
Minerals have been extracted on the eastern flank of Dartmoor for centuries. These include tin, copper, silver, lead, iron, zinc, manganese and arsenic. As Dartmoor rivers the Teign and the

Bovey both powered mine sites. The Beadon Brook, a Teign tributary, powered wheels at Hennock silver lead mine and others at the iron mine at Great Rock. Frank Mills, Wheal Exmouth, the Teign Valley Barytes Mine, Birch Aller Mine, Wheal Lawrence and Wheal Anna Maria all employed water power as did several earlier tinners' mills upstream. Sites on Bovey streams included East Vitifer, New Vitifer, Great Wheal Eleanor, Yarner Copper Mine and Kelly Mine.

Waterwheels were used for pumping, powering stamps for crushing ores, for working buddles and bellows for smelting. They were typically overshot.

Tinners' mills
The Bovey and the Teign had their share of tin blowing mills and stamping mills (knocking mills) for working the tin ore extracted by tin streaming and from open works. The mills date from the years 1450 to 1650 and only a few ruined walls are the most that remain at these sites.

Fulling and woollen mills
Bovey Tracey parish had a functioning fulling mill in 1327: in the south west fulling mills were known as tucking mills. Chagford had a woollen industry in the first half of the nineteenth century, following development by Richard Berry of Ashburton. Fulling mills also existed at Moretonhampstead. In the early nineteenth century Parkway Mill at Chudleigh was used for spinning wool for worsted cloth.

Pottery and flint mills
Bovey Pottery made extensive use of water power, preparing clay in pug mills and for several other purposes, including flint mills at the pottery and at Jews Bridge, Teigngrace. Calcined flints, imported from elsewhere, were powdered in slurry grinding pans and used in slipwares; to provide glazes to turn earthenware pottery into creamwares.

Iron mills
Iron Mills at Dunsford were equipped with water-powered tilt hammers – usually referred to as trip hammers in the south west – and made edge tools – bill hooks, scythes and thatchers' tools. Ashton Mills briefly also had tilt hammers and a blast for making iron. Reap hooks and shovels were made here in 1804.

Tanneries
Devon was an ideal location for oak-bark tanneries. The bark was ground into powder to mix with water to make tannic acid, used in manufacturing leather from hides. Devon had the cattle – Ruby Reds had the best hides; oak woods were abundant and there was plenty of water to power the bark mills. There were three known tanneries at Moretonhampstead and one at Chudleigh but only Steward Mill at Moreton was known to have employed a water-powered bark mill. Large tanneries existed nearby, at Newton Abbot.

Saw mills
With its wooded valleys it is not surprising that water-powered saw mills existed on east Dartmoor. Yeo Mill at Chagford was one such site; Veet Mill at Drewsteignton was another. The woollen mill near Chagford Bridge was converted to a saw mill following the closure of the textile industry there.

Leats and weirs
Leats could be very short, as at Foxworthy Mill, Lustleigh, or at Wyndhurst, Throwleigh. But in some cases they were often quite long: 2,950 yards (2,698m) from weir to mill at New Mill, North Bovey; one mile long to Frog Mill, Throwleigh; half a mile (0.8km) long to Rushford Mill, Chagford; three-quarters of a mile (1.2km) long to Town Mills, Bovey Tracey.

The leat to Bovey Pottery, taken from the Becka Brook, above Becky Falls, was constructed in the nineteenth century, and was over four miles long. It was in use into the 1950s.

Weirs on the Teign were often major hydraulic structures – for example at Bridford Mills, Fingle Mill, Moretonhampstead, and above Steps Bridge, Dunsford. There is evidence to suggest the weir serving Farley Mill, Chagford, was intended to be rebuilt further upstream in the 1820s and a new leat channel cut. Some of the Teign weirs were sketched by Reverend Swete in the last decade of the eighteenth century.

Mine leats could be more extensive. The Southill tinners' leat in Chagford parish, extant in the fifteenth century, was over five miles long. In the sixteenth century a 12-mile-long (19.2km) leat was cut from the Walla and Gallaven brooks on Dartmoor to the Bradford tinwork in Drewsteignton parish, allegedly crossing a valley at West Week on a 22-foot high (6.7m) launder, 440 yards (402m) long.

Floods and fires

Mills were prone to flooding. Sited on leats, millers had some control in preventing floods by opening sluice gates or hatches upstream on the leat, allowing the water to bypass the mill. The miller's son was often given this task; he might have to venture out at night, in the middle of a storm, with a lantern.

Palace Mill and Chudleigh Bridge Mill, on the Kate Brook, were both flooded in 1875. There were no doubt other mills that were affected, but often flooding went unreported.

Grain mills were prone to fires. Millstones left running unattended, with grain running out, could create a fire. But not all fires were started this way. Weir Mill, Drewsteignton was destroyed by an incendiary in 1833. At Uppacott farm, Moretonhampstead, where water-power was employed, arson was probably the cause when a barn containing wheat, barley and oats was destroyed in 1851. Fingle Mill, in the same parish, burnt down in 1894. Iron Mills at Dunsford were seriously damaged by fire in 1891. The new four-storey Town Mills at Bovey Tracey were destroyed in 1925 together with 2,000 sacks of

flour and wheat. Town Mills, Chudleigh, which had been damaged in that town's great fire in 1807, was again affected in 1858 and in 1941 when a conflagration destroyed the miller's house.

Farm mills

The mid nineteenth century was the golden age of farming. In the decades from 1830 to 1880 landowners improved their estates by introducing water power to work threshing machines, apple pulpers, chaff cutters and milling equipment for animal feed. Sites include Stone at Bridford; Clifford Farm, Moreton; Whiddon Park and Rushford Barton at Chagford; Furlong, Drewsteignton; Plumley and Southbrook, Bovey Tracey, Water at Manaton and West Coombe in North Bovey parish.

Millers

A miller often employed others to help run his mill. A stoneman would look after the running of the mill and dress the millstones; a spoutsman would bag the flour, while the miller might have another assistant working in an adjoining bakery. A carter would bring grain to the mill and deliver flour and sometimes bread to customers.

Chudleigh, 1795. An unidentified site, but which may have been Town Mills before rebuilding, and the town's fire of 1807. However in 1792 Town Mills were advertised for sale as 'the well-accustomed three water grist mills', which might suggest more than the one overshot waterwheel seen here. Parkway Mill is the alternative site.
Courtesy Devon Heritage Services, image reference SC0342

Ashton Mills had a bakehouse in 1785. A bakery was added at Lustleigh Mill in the nineteenth century. The Bovey Mills, Bovey Tracey, supported at least three bakers in the town. At Drewsteignton, Veet Mill appears to have supported three bakers in the village before it was converted to a saw mill. There were also bakers at East Mill, Manaton, and at Bowden Mill, North Bovey, in the Victorian era.

Country millers were to some degree self sufficient. Their mills often came with an orchard. Mature apple, pear and crab apple woods were ideal for making cogs for the mill's gear train, when dried and cut into boards. Beech was quite often used, too. Apparently whitebeam, hornbeam and ash were also employed up country, as well as holly and box. Millers often kept pigs. They would thrive on spilt grain, bran or apples. And in earlier centuries tallow was used to lubricate the mill cogs.

The Perryman family at Yeo Mill, Chagford, lived there for over four hundred years. Members of the Hole family were at Lustleigh Mill for at least eighty years and the Tarr family were associated with Rushford Mill, Chagford, for over a hundred years. The Surridge family milled at Bridford Mills for over seventy years until at least 1921. But other mills changed hands frequently and were often leased from landowners.

Ugbrooke House and Park. Home of the Clifford family.
Postcard by Chapman and Son/ author's collection

Haldon House with the Belvedere on the hill above. The Belvedere still stands but the most of house has been demolished. It belonged to the Palk family.
Originally drawn by William LePetit. Courtesy Devon Heritage Services, image reference SC1385.

Landowners

Quite a number of mill sites and mines were owned by some of Devon's leading families in the nineteenth and early twentieth centuries. The Earls of Devon, who resided at Powderham Castle, owned the Bovey Pottery site, a mine at North Bovey and other mill sites in Moretonhampstead. Some of these properties came into the hands of Lord Hambleden, the son of W. H. Smith, who built North Bovey Manor House, now known as Bovey Castle. The Palk family, of the now largely-demolished Haldon House, owned sites in the Teign valley and at Hennock. Lord Exmouth of Canonteign and Teignmouth owned Ashton Mills and much of Ashton parish together with mines in the Teign valley. The Cliffords of Ugbrooke House owned mills in Chudleigh and Kingsteignton; the Fulfords of Great Fulford owned a mine sett in Dunsford parish.

Ironfounders, millwrights and engineers

Seventeenth- and eighteenth-century watermill machinery was largely wooden and involved skilled carpentry. Waterwheels, shafts and gears were often constructed of oak; elm was also used for gears. The establishment of local iron foundries in the early nineteenth century led to the availability of cast iron for wheels, gears and other machinery.

Henry Beare had the nearest foundry to the Teign and the Bovey – at Liverton. He started his career as a millwright. A large overshot waterwheel was installed by him at Hedge Barton, on Dartmoor, in the late 1840s. It was cast for him by Martin & Parkin of Exeter. Beare later moved to Newton Abbot, where he competed with two other ironfounders – Webber and Polyblank. Several Beare waterwheels survive including Bagtor Mill, by the river Lemon, just outside the study area, and Coombe Farm, Moretonhampstead, which is within it. At New Mill, North Bovey, the penstock and parts of the machinery are his work.

A Polyblank & Co wheel exists in situ at Yeo, Chagford. At Ashton Mill the undershot waterwheel was supplied by Stenner & Gunn of Tiverton, in the twentieth century. The firm still exists today. Willcocks of Buckfastleigh was another local ironfounder. A small overshot waterwheel by this firm survives at Kelly Mine. Many of the Teign valley mills relied on Bodley Bros of Exeter for mill gears and other ironwork. Bodleys, and their offshoot Taylor and Bodley, were specialists in the production of cast-iron bevel gears. They also supplied specialist equipment for saw mills, paper mills and tanneries.

In more recent times waterwheels have been imported from outside the county. Holy Street Mill has a waterwheel cast by G. H. Harris of Wadebridge and Steward Mill has one by Bartle of Carn Brea – both Cornish ironfounders. At Kelly Mine, a 16ft overshot, which previously worked at Chubworthy Farm in Somerset, has recently been restored to working order. There were several millwrights and machinists at work in the district. Near Bridford Mill, Joseph Wills ran the Teign Valley Machine Works from at least 1861 until 1890 when the premises were for sale. Equipment included a waterwheel and a chaff cutter. Wills was variously described as a millwright, a wheelwright and a mechanic.

Better known perhaps were John and William Dicker of Chagford. An 1857 trade directory listed them as *'Wheelwrights, engineers and machinists'*. Elsewhere they were recorded as agricultural implement makers. They would have commissioned ironfounders from Exeter or Newton Abbot to cast their waterwheels.

The last waterwheel to work at Fingle Mill, Moretonhampstead was cast for them. Naves from two separate waterwheels survive here. The extant low-breastshot wheel at Sandy Park Mill – now the Mill End Hotel – is theirs, as is the large overshot in the converted barn at East Wrey, Lustleigh. The overshot waterwheel at New Mill, North Bovey, is another Dicker product. They made threshing machines too – one was for sale at Rushford Barton in 1868.

In the 1860s the Dickers employed George Henry Reed, the son of a naval captain, to train as an engineer and machinist. By 1870 he had established his own business at Rushford Works near Rushford Bridge. He also set up the Chagford and Devon Electric Light Company, which first lit the town in September 1891. Power was generated by the waterwheel in the old woollen mill at Factory Cross near Chagford Bridge.
Reed's one surviving waterwheel is dated 1892. It was installed at Foxworthy in 1978 to generate electricity. It may have been cast for him by Bodley Bros; in 1883 he had ordered a 12ft diameter overshot wheel from them with 36 buckets [DHC – 67/5/2/3 folio 979].

Hydropower

In 1914 the Chagford company replaced the waterwheel at the Factory with a 30hp turbine, thought to be of American manufacture. Several other hydropower installations followed – for example two turbines were installed on the banks of the Teign to provide electricity for Castle Drogo.

Turbines were also used by the mining industry. Kelly Mine has one by Gilbert Gilkes of Kendal. Sowton Mill, at Dunsford, had a turbine in 1950, which was replaced in 1986. Upstream a modern Archimedean screw turbine, working off the Sowton leat, was commissioned in autumn 2013. Other recent hydropower installations are at Bowden Mill, Ashton Mills and at Holy Street.

In 1957 hydropower was employed at Fernworthy Reservoir: a small turbine generated electricity for the dam-keeper's cottage. Not all hydropower installations employed turbines. At Yeo Mill, Chagford, and at Blackaton and Wyndhurst, in Throwleigh, waterwheels did the work, as did the G. H. Reed wheel at Foxworthy Mill.

Into the modern era

Country grain mills began to become uncompetitive towards the end of the nineteenth century. Steam power and roller milling technology encouraged industrial-scale milling at ports such as Avonmouth and Plymouth. The hard North American grains produced flour better suited for bread making, whereas the softer English grains found use as animal feed.

Imported grain was distributed by the railway network to local stations; the line to Moreton-hampstead from Newton Abbot opened in July 1866 and a branch from Heathfield to Ashton followed in 1882.

By the end of the nineteenth century the decline in country milling had set in. At some locations milling was combined with farming.

Surviving mills

Not a single watermill survives in working order on the Teign or its tributaries. Some mills have been demolished, others have become house conversions.

Waterwheels have been preserved or restored in places, as at Iron Mills, Dunsford, where billhooks are still made, but the hammers are no longer water powered. A visit to Sticklepath is worthwhile: at the National Trust's Finch Foundry a water-powered trip hammer is still demonstrated.

Devon is fortunate that a few of its grain mills have been restored to some extent. Two of the nearest to the Teign catchment area are Town Mill, Totnes and Cricklepit Mill, Exeter; the latter the headquarters of the Devon Wildlife Trust. Both are accessible to the visitor at certain times.

For the most complete example of a small Dartmoor mining enterprise, Kelly Mine retains two waterwheels. Its preservation society holds an open day, usually once every two years. Several mills can be seen from nearby roads. Other sites can be glimpsed from public footpaths – for example paths run past Sowton Mill, the site of Frog Mill, Foxworthy Mill and Rushford Mill.

Mills on the Teign

The Teign valley at Fingle Bridge. From a Chapman and Son postcard

Water-powered sites – including grain mills and mines – in Chagford, Chudleigh, Christow, Dunsford, Drewsteignton, Gidleigh, Throwleigh and other nearby parishes together with some in Moretonhampstead

Notes to the gazetteer

Abbreviations

DHC	Devon Heritage Centre, Sowton, Exeter
DTRG	Dartmoor Tinworking Research Group
EH	English Heritage
n. d.	no date
RAMM	Royal Albert Memorial Museum, Exeter
SHC	Somerset Heritage Centre, Taunton
TNA	The National Archives, Kew

Weights and measures

Imperial units are generally adopted in the text as they were the units in use when the mills were operational, some time before decimalisation. But note that the dimensions of tinners' mills are provided in metres.

Acre, A or a	1 acre = 4,840 square yards or 0.405 hectares
Bushel	A bushel of wheat weighed 56 lbs or 25.4 kilograms
cuft	Cubic feet
Fathom	A unit of length = six feet (1.8 metres)
ft	Foot or feet. 1 foot = 30.48 centimetres
Gallon	1 gallon = 4.546 litres
Hogshead	1 hogshead = 54 gallons
H.P., hp	Horse power. 1 hp = 746 watts
lb	Pound weight. 1 lb = 0.45359237 kilograms
kW	Kilowatt
R or r	Rood. 1 rood = 0.1 hectares
rpm	Revolutions per minute
P or p	Perch. 1 perch = 0.00625 acre
Quarter	1 quarter = 28 lbs or 12.70058 kilograms
Sack	a West of England sack full of wheat weighed 280 lbs
V	Volt
Yard	A unit of length = 3 feet

National grid references

Watermill sites have, as far as possible, been provided with an 8-figure Ordnance Survey national grid reference (ngr). Mine setts are designated with 6-figure ngrs whereas small tin blowing and stamping mills are located with 8-figure ngrs.

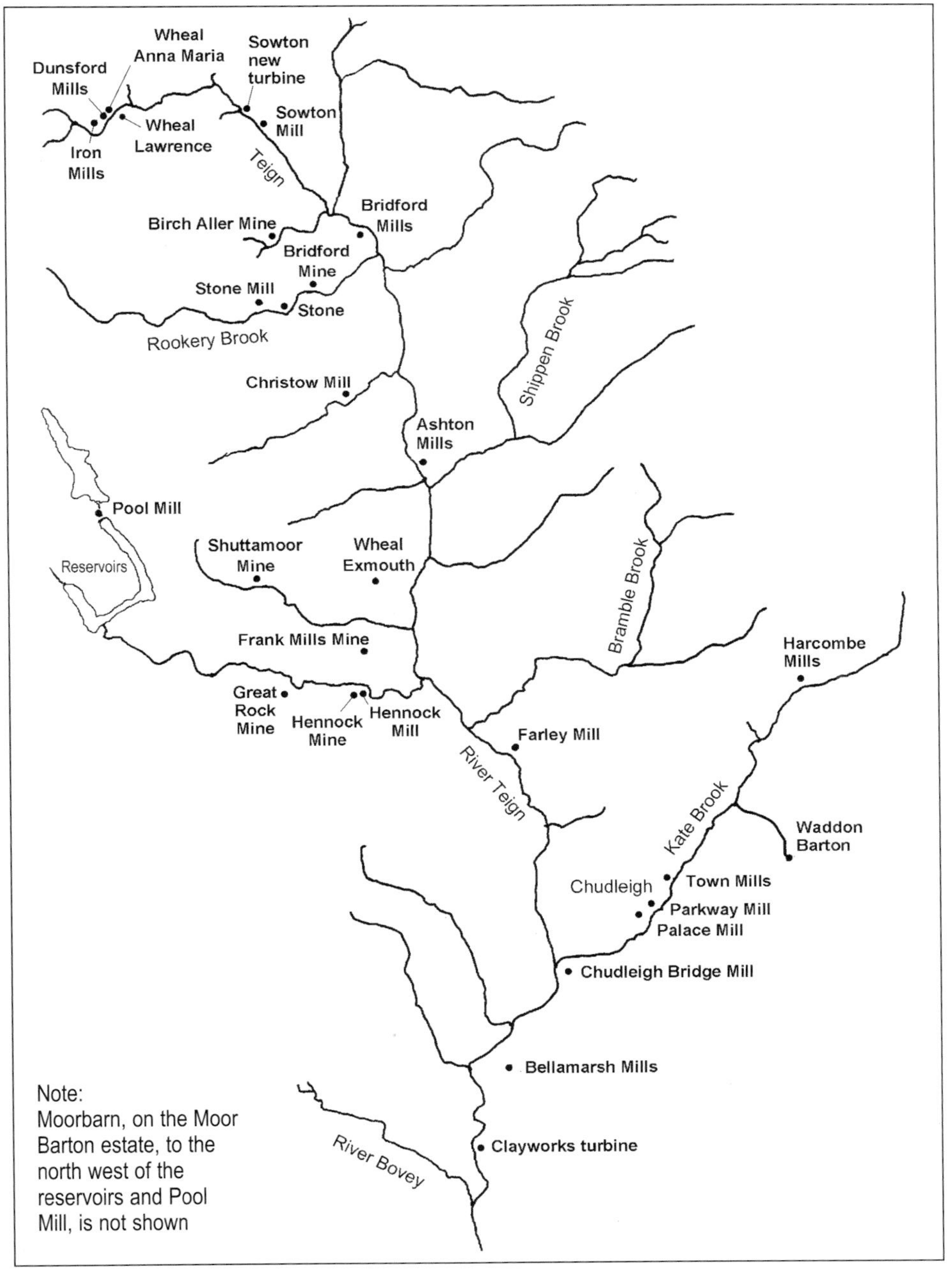

Mills on the Teign – upstream to Dunsford

The Teign from its confluence with the Bovey to Dunsford, including mills on the Kate Brook and other tributaries.
The sequence of mills in the gazetteer runs upstream

Map labels:
Dunsford Mills
Wheal Anna Maria
Sowton new turbine
Sowton Mill
Wheal Lawrence
Iron Mills
Teign
Birch Aller Mine
Bridford Mills
Bridford Mine
Stone Mill
Stone
Rookery Brook
Shippen Brook
Christow Mill
Ashton Mills
Pool Mill
Reservoirs
Shuttamoor Mine
Wheal Exmouth
Bramble Brook
Frank Mills Mine
Harcombe Mills
Great Rock Mine
Hennock Mine
Hennock Mill
Farley Mill
River Teign
Kate Brook
Waddon Barton
Chudleigh
Town Mills
Parkway Mill
Palace Mill
Chudleigh Bridge Mill
Bellamarsh Mills
Clayworks turbine
River Bovey

Note:
Moorbarn, on the Moor Barton estate, to the north west of the reservoirs and Pool Mill, is not shown

15

Bellamarsh Mills, Kingsteignton

SX 8520 7720

Bellamarsh Mills were demolished in 1973 when the Chudleigh bypass was constructed; this now forms part of the A38 Devon Expressway. Fortunately photographs of the mill, taken by Alan Stoyel, survive. The mills and their machinery were surveyed and drawn by Bruce Bolton: his work was said to have been deposited in the Royal Albert Memorial Museum. [1]

The three-storey mill building was five bays long with a slate roof. [2] This relatively large structure was equipped with two breastshot waterwheels and was noted as *'newly-built'* in 1864. [3] The waterwheels were powered by a 910-yard-long leat from a weir on the Teign. This was the lowest grain mill on the river: the fall of water below the mills to the tidal estuary near Newton Abbot was slight.

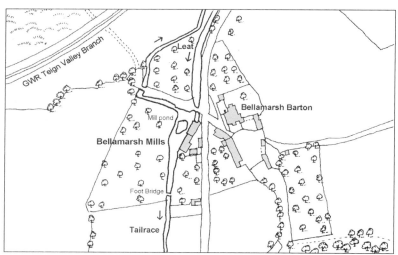

Bellamarsh Mills in 1889. The leat from the Teign runs in from the north. The overflow doubles back to the river and the tailrace runs on to the south and in 1909 was extended to form the leat to a water turbine at Etson Marshes, by Newbridge, to power clay workings. The course of the Great Western Railway's Teign Valley Branch is now the A38 Exeter-Plymouth Devon Expressway

There was an earlier mill on the site in 1731. In 1794 the business was being run by J. Ball & Co. [4] Around the turn of the century, when the price of bread meant that it was often out of reach of the poor, the mill was attacked by a mob and gutted. One of the rioters, Campion, a carpenter – but he may have been a blacksmith, and possibly innocent – was publicly hanged on Bovey Heathfield as an example to others. [5]

In 1815, when the mill was owned by Lord Templer of Stover House, Teigngrace, it was being worked by William and James Couch. It was then offered to let:

'.. all those Capital and Well accustomed GRIST and FLOUR MILLS, which mills have a constant and abundant supply of water, from the River Teign, and consist of four pair of stones, two water wheels, a cleaning and bunting machine, a threshing and winnowing machine of sufficient power to thresh and clean near 10 bags of wheat or twelve bags of barley an hour, .. with three Acres of Orchard, and 9 Acres of Meadow Land. Also the Salmon Fishery on the River Teign ..' [6]

Daniel Whiteway and Company ran the business as millers, corn factors and as managers of the Teign fishery in 1819. Whiteway's partner was John Hatherley of Fishwick, Kingsteignton. [7] Whiteway's rent was £170 per annum, payable to Lord Clifford, who had become the owner: this would be equivalent to about £12,000 in today's money. [8]

By 1848 Mr Honeywell was miller and part of the grist mill was given over to processing manganese ore, which was mined further up the Teign valley. [9] Thomas Searell was here in 1851. He was born at Staverton. By 1861 he was recorded as a corn and flour merchant of Bellamarsh, employing five men, as well as a cook, a housemaid and a nurse for his younger sons.[10] He advertised the mill for sale or to let in 1864. The newly-built mill came with a dwelling house, two cottages, stabling and 14 acres of land, mostly pasture and orchard.[11]

Milling was undertaken by John White in 1877 - 1885. He advertised the mill for sale in 1877 and 1882.[12] But he, (or his son), was still active here in 1885, when advertising for a carter.[13] After the First World War Edwin Raymont was listed as miller.[14] At some date before 1927 Bellamarsh had a turbine installed. This was still operating in the decade to 1960. It drove two pairs of 4ft 6in millstones. The other two pairs were powered by the remaining low breastshot waterwheel.[15] This

wheel is now at Town Mills, Totnes, on the Dart, where it can be seen today.[16] It was refurbished and fitted with new wooden paddles.

In 1909 the tailrace from Bellamarsh Mill was extended into a 1520-yard-long leat that powered a **water turbine at Etson Marshes, Newbridge** – at SX 8487 7626. This turned a dynamo initially to provide power to several clay workings. When this proved unsuccessful, rope drives were installed, some between a quarter and half a mile distant from the turbine.[17]

Bellamarsh Mill in August 1960.
Far left: the surviving breastshot waterwheel. It was 14ft by 6ft 3in with 16in wide floats or paddles and was estimated to generate up to 18.5hp, but in practice about 14hp.[18] It was removed to Ugbrooke Park and was later installed at Town Mill, Totnes, by Martin Watts.
Left: the drive from the turbine.
Above: the mill in 1960, rear elevation. The building was demolished in 1973.
All photographs by Alan Stoyel

Chudleigh Bridge Mill, Chudleigh

SX 8590 7838

Chudleigh Bridge Mill, disused in 1794. Watercolour by Rev. John Swete. This mill and its replacement were both extant at that date.
Courtesy Devon Heritage Services, image reference 564M/F6/55

In the late eighteenth century the old watermill – seen above – was replaced by a new building. When Reverend Swete visited Chudleigh in April 1794 he saw both mills at Chudleigh Bridge:
'.. the whole assemblage of objects here, was of the most .. picturesque Nature: the shed in the foreground the Antient Mill, which being superseded by its Neighbour has ceas'd to perform its revolutions, the gothic arch in the gable end of the building, almost over-run by the now unmolested ivy - the woods of Bellemarsh, the River Teign, the distant hills, were all features of a Beautiful cast, and uniting together form an extremely pleasing Landscape.'[1]

There are references to both a fulling mill – Lawell Tucking Mill – and a grist mill on or near this site. It may also have been known as Shipperidge Mills or Sheperidge Mill; the name occurs in a deed of 1597.[2] Water power was provided by a leat from the Kate Brook. John

Whiteway, the miller at Town Mills, Chudleigh in 1841,[3] advertised for a sub-tenant for the grain mill at Chudleigh Bridge in 1844:
'Chudleigh Bridge Mills, In the said Parish, with a never-failing stream of water, driving three pairs of stones, by two water wheels, Bolting Mills, &c, and about two acres of Meadow, Orchard &c.'[4]

He was bankrupt in 1845 and was in serious trouble:
'John Whiteway was indicted for stealing on the 15th of Aug., at Chudleigh Bridge Mills, three millstones, the property of Hugh, Lord Clifford .. the prisoner, a baker and miller of Chudleigh, had become bankrupt in 1845. His assignees sold his interest in the mills he had occupied under Lord Clifford, and the possession of them passed to Mr Thomas Sanders, who became the immediate tenant under Lord Clifford, a man named William Dennis being the under tenant of Sanders, as he had been of prisoner previously. Sanders occupied the mills .. until the middle of 1847 ..

Whiteway then applied to Sanders to become the under tenant; but as he was an uncertificated bankrupt Sanders refused, unless he could give security for the rent. Sanders then went with the prisoner to Mr Knight, Lord Clifford's steward, to use his interest that the prisoner might be taken as tenant instead of himself, as he (Sanders) found it a losing concern. Mr Knight, however, refused ..

.. An arrangement was then made between Sanders and the prisoner, and the prisoner was permitted to work the mill. But Sanders, finding that Lord Clifford looked to him for rent, and the overseers came on him for taxes, gave Whiteway notice to quit, and ultimately went down with a constable and carpenter, and turned Whiteway out of the mill. The three upper millstones .. the

subject of this indictment, were then at work in the mill. Some short time after .. Sanders, as the mill was unoccupied, surrendered the lease to Lord Clifford .. who took .. possession of the premises. On doing this Sanders took off the upper mill stones to prevent them being worked... On the 18th April Sanders .. went to the mill and found the stones missing ..

A reward was offered for the discovery of the felons, and search made, on which the stones were found .. concealed in a shed or barn in a field, in .. Kingsteignton .. a new tenant came in; and the stones were delivered by Mr Sanders to a millwright, ..Dormer, who made them fit for work .. on the morning of the 15th, the locks had been broken .. and these three valuable stones .. were missing again. Sanders, with the assistance of Charles Strowbridge, Lord Clifford's bailiff, followed the tracks of carts to the door of the prisoner's house in Chudleigh ..

.. Dominic Dormer, the millwright, said the stones were worth £20 ..; "one was a French, another a Welsh stone, and the third a French stone with a moor eye"; he identified them as those which were found in Haye's yard .. While he was standing there in the yard, prisoner came up and said they were his stones and he would have them. Prisoner .. came into the yard again with fifteen or twenty men, who rolled the stones into prisoner's premises, from which they were removed by Moyle the constable, with a warrant...

For the defence Mr Bird admitted that the prisoner took the stones but did so under the impression however erroneous that he had a right to take them .. the learned counsel .. attributed this prosecution to malice .. and commenting very severely on the evidence of Mr Sanders .. the prisoner was acquitted.' [5]

Chudleigh Bridge Mill. The late eighteenth-century mill, disused in 1899. In 1844 two waterwheels drove three pairs of stones; only one is evident in this photograph. *Chudleigh History Group*

John Pooke, 29, from Hennock, was miller in 1851, assisted by Joseph Ganniccliffe, also a Hennock man. [6] Samuel Whale ran the mill in 1861. [7] Henry Metherell, born in Combeinteignhead in about 1835, was miller from 1873 to 1890.

The mill suffered in a flood in 1875: *'Chudleigh. Lower Kidbrook Bridge was washed away by the force of the torrent. .. At Chudleigh Bridge Mills, occupied by Mr Metherall [sic], over forty bushels of wheat were washed out of the mill. The turnpike road adjoining was torn up by the rush of water and left a fissure several feet deep, and seven feet wide ..'* [8]

Metherell moved to Palace Mill in 1890 and milling ceased here. The mill building saw use by the White family, who farmed here. It was demolished before the Second World War. [9]

Palace or Place Mill, Chudleigh

SX 8680 7891

This was the second mill on the Kate Brook, going upstream. Palace or Place was an estate in 1794, consisting of a farm or barton, a lime quarry with kilns and housing for lime burners, including a *'counting house'* and a *'very good set of griest mills in complete repair which .. may be converted into sawing mills'*.
William Bickford was the tenant. [1]

Lord Clifford owned the mill in 1838 when it was being run by John Wotton. [2] Wotton was born in about 1772 at Kingsteignton. In 1851, aged 79, he employed his two sons William, 47, and Daniel, 40, as millers and three labourers to work the 44-acre farm. [3] Wotton died in 1858 and the leasehold was for sale the following year, when the estate was occupied by Daniel Wotton. [4]

Robert Hall was miller in 1861. He suffered a loss in 1875 when Palace Mills was inundated with flood water; grain, flour and a ploughing machine were all damaged. [5] More serious was a fire in March 1877. The Exeter Flying Post carried this report:

Palace Mill, Chudleigh, upstream side, before conversion. August 1960. The internal waterwheel was later removed and re-installed at Water, Manaton.
Alan Stoyel

'Chudleigh. Destructive Fire. This little town was on Wednesday visited by .. the destruction by fire of an extensive mill and machinery, with the adjacent house and granaries belonging to Lord Clifford and occupied by Mr Robert Hall. No doubt is entertained that the fire was incendiary in its origin and when once set burning the heavy gale which raged through the day spread the flames so rapidly that it was impossible to save anything. The fire engine was on the spot in a very short time, but was almost powerless .. The mill, machinery and stores are totally destroyed. The destruction of the grain, including about 2,000 bushels of wheat, not insured to their full value, entails a heavy loss on Mr Hall. Nothing is now left standing but the shell of the building ..' [6]

Lord Clifford required Hall to rebuild the house, mill, and poundhouse, with all necessary machinery and gear, at his own expense, before the next Lady-day. [7] The mill was rebuilt and in 1884 Hall left; in 1891 he was listed as retired miller at the Lower Mills, Kingsteignton, his son Robert H. Hall running the business at Chudleigh. [8]

The leasehold was for sale in January 1891 and an outline of the mill was given in the Western Times:
'.. To be Let by Private Contract all those Corn and Flour Mills, known as Palace Mills, Chudleigh .. together with a good Dwelling-House and eight acres of Land and all necessary Outbuildings. The Mills contain three pair of Stones, two for wheat and one for barley, also silk flour Dressing Machine, and improved Victor Smut Machine, driven by a powerful overshot waterwheel, and a never failing stream of water. There is also a custom cider pound driven by the water wheel, which the taker will be required to buy off together with the cider making utensils ..' [9]

Robert's elder son John M. Hall moved to the next mill upstream, Parkway, where he was milling in 1891.[10] The Metherells moved into Palace Mill from Chudleigh Bridge, but the son John, 27, died of a heart attack in 1897.[11] Daniel Hookway was the new miller. Born in Sandford, he had had experience of milling at Dowrich Mill, near Crediton; at Cricklepit Mill, Exeter; at mills at Winchester and Bishop's Waltham in Hampshire and at Beare Mill, Crediton, where he suffered a fire which destroyed the building in 1897.[12]

Then his sons William and Walter ran Palace Mills until their bankruptcy.[13] Milling may have ceased around 1902. In 1910 the premises were advertised to let to woodworkers with water power to work *'light machinery'*.[14]

The mill gearing and the internal overshot waterwheel remained throughout much of the twentieth century, but a flood in the 1960s scoured the bed of the Kate Brook upstream rendering the leat high and dry. The mill was for sale in 1988, the machinery was removed and the building converted to three residential units.[15] The gearing went to Collacombe Barton, Lamerton, where it was seen stored in April 2000. The waterwheel went to Water, Manaton.[16]

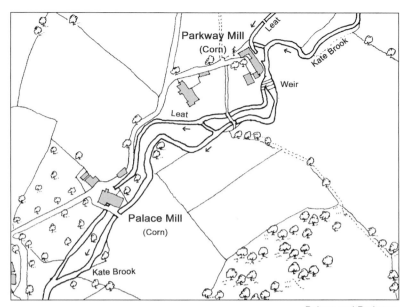

Palace and Parkway Mills, from the 1888 Ordnance Survey map

Palace Mill, downstream side; undergoing conversion in July 1989. *Alan Stoyel*

Parkway or Park Mill, Chudleigh
SX 8694 7904

This site is well documented and there are at least three references to it in the second half of the seventeenth century. In 1650 and 1681 it was known as three mills called Park or Parke Mills.[1] Leases from 1753 refer to three grist mills and a malt mill.[2] 'Three mills' suggest separate sets of gearing powered by two or three independent waterwheels. The mill was powered by a leat from the Kate Brook.

Robert Wood of Alphington, a miller, insured a house and millhouse here in 1777; the buildings were recorded as *'stone and cob built and slated and thatched'*. His tenant was Robert Knight.[3] Parke Mills, containing *'.. a compleat set of grist mills, with bunting for the flour trade; a dwelling house ..'*, were to be sold by auction in 1790.[4]

Parkway Mill, Chudleigh. The front of the mill seen in 1960; since converted to a residence, now known as 'The Granary'. The overshot waterwheel was on the far side of the building
Alan Stoyel

Conversion followed. Machinery for spinning wool for worsted cloth was installed by Bailey and Leare. In 1797 Parkway was known as White's Mills; William Bailey was the proprietor. He was succeeded by Samuel Paul Bamford, here in 1818, and the site was known as *'Mills, late White's and Factory'*. [5] On his death in 1823 the mills were offered for sale:

'Late in the occupation of Mr Samuel P. Bamford, deceased, and used for spinning worsted yarn, near adjoining the town of Chudleigh, and constantly supplied with a good stream of water, with all the various articles of machinery .. For viewing the Premises apply at the house and for further particulars .. Mr Caunter, Ashburton.' [6]

From about 1825 Mr Pearce of Exeter ran the 'Factory', and from 1832 he was in partnership with a Mr Horsey. William Bailey retained

ownership of the mills [7] but in 1834 the machinery was auctioned:

'Worsted Machinery. Chudleigh Mill .. FOUR WORSTED SPINNING FRAMES, of Ninety-six Spindles each, with PREPARERS equal thereto, the whole of which is of the best principle, and in good condition. Also, many gross of Drawing, Slubbing, Roving, and Spinning BOBBINS, Seven Pair Warping Bars, Skeiners and other articles necessary for the manufacture of Worsted, &c &c. The whole will be put in lots as may be determined on the day of sale. The premises are to be applied to another purpose.
For further particulars, apply to Mr. PEARSE, Rack Street, Exeter ..' [8]

John Wotton owned Parkway Mill in 1838, when it was known as 'Hemen's Mill'. He was also milling at Palace Mill. He would appear to have been responsible for converting the premises back to grain milling. Parkway was still known as 'Factory' and 'Factory House' in the 1841 census. In the 1851 census the site was recorded as 'Buley's Mill'. William Wotton was probably miller from about 1850 to 1860. [9] The freehold was for sale in 1860:

'.. old-established and well-accustomed Water Grist Mills, called Factory Mills, otherwise Parkway Mills, situated within a quarter-of-a-mile of Chudleigh, together with the Outbuildings, Cottage, and about half an acre of Orchard, belonging and contiguous.
The Mills are supplied with an unfailing stream of water, driving two pairs of stones, are well fitted with complete machinery and mill gear .. To view the property apply to Mr. William Wotton, on the Premises ..' [10]

William Wotton was still resident in 1861. [11] The mills were to let in 1864, described as *'recently rebuilt .. fitted up with new gear, working two pair of French stones .. smut and flour machines with convenient corn and flour hutches.'* [12] Richard White milled here briefly but departed in 1866. [13] William Wotton, now at the Ship Inn, Chudleigh, offered the mills to let in 1869. [14] Samuel Ball, who had worked Farley Mills on the Teign, moved here in about 1870 and stayed at least until 1881. By that time he was assisted by his son John, aged 23. [15]

A flood caused damage in October 1875: *'Chudleigh .. At Parkway Mills, occupied by Mr Ball, the water was six feet deep, and consequently damaged a great deal of corn and flour. The premises were also much injured, and it is estimated that the damage, including the destruction of a stable, will amount to £100. Mr. Ball's loss is estimated at £50.'* [16]

By 1884 John Maddicott Hall, son of Robert Hall of Palace Mill, was resident: he was advertising for a general miller in October. [17] He was still milling in 1891, but the mill was offered to let in 1895. [18]

In 1901 he was recorded at Parkway as farmer and dairy keeper [19] and the mill was for sale: *'To be sold by auction .. on May 20. The Parkway Mills, close to the town of Chudleigh. The mill is worked by an overshot water wheel, driving two pairs of wheat stones and one pair of barley stones.'* It was also equipped with Thornton's patent flour silk, Smith's purifier, Eureka smut machine, flour silk, hutches and hoisting gear. [20]

At some time after 1860 an extra pair of stones and associated gearing had been installed. The freehold estate, which included a residence and a cottage, failed to reach its reserve and was withdrawn from sale. [21]

Parkway Mill was probably redundant in 1902. Chudleigh Electric Light and Power Company used the site to house its generating equipment in the years from 1929 to 1947. After the Second World War the mill house was run as a hotel. [22]

Today both mill house and mill survive; the mill is now a residence renamed 'The Granary'.

Town Mills, Chudleigh

SX 8707 7934
Listed Grade II. English Heritage ID: 1097099

Near the foot of Clifford Street, earlier known as Mill Lane, where it crosses the Kate Brook, there were *'washing and tucking'* fields which suggest Town Mills was once involved in the woollen industry, as a fulling mill; tucking being the west country term for this process. [1]

The Ewens family were millers in the years 1711-1780. Joseph Widdicombe ran the mill from at least 1788 until his death in July 1792. [2] Town Mills were for sale in August that year, detailed as *'the well-accustomed three water grist mills'*. A dwelling house, stabling and other outhouses, herb gardens and orchard were included in the sale. [3] Three grist mills might indicate that the building at that time employed three water wheels; it may however suggest that there were two overshot waterwheels in line. By the late sixteenth century mill gearing had developed sufficiently for one waterwheel to power two sets of millstones. [4]

John Whiteway took possession of the property and it was occupied by John Wotton, a relative, until 1802; Wotton then moved downstream to Parkway Mill. About this time the leat, which runs for about a mile from Hams Barton, was improved using French prisoners of war. A French coin dated 1792 was found during restoration work in 1971. [5]

John Whiteway the younger was the miller in 1807 when the mill suffered some damage in the great fire of Chudleigh: it was on the edge of the conflagration. Following his death in 1826 he was succeeded by his widow Susanna and then, by 1830, William Whiteway. Walter Whiteway had the mill in 1833 and Samuel in 1836.[6] He held the freehold in 1838.[7] In 1841 Samuel, 25, a maltster, and his elder brother John ran the mill. Following John's bankruptcy in 1845, Samuel took charge of Town Mills; John had been left Luton Mill, near Ideford, by his father.[8]

Samuel advertised the mill in 1846:
'To be Sold in Fee at Public Auction .. Lot 2. All those extensive Flour and Grist Mills called the Town Mills .. situated in .. Chudleigh, driving three pair of French stones with all necessary gear and worked by a never failing stream of water, in which 100 sacks of flour per week may with ease be made; also an excellent Dwelling

House adjoining the Mills, with Yard, Stabling, and all necessary Outbuildings, together with a thrashing machine worked by water; adjoining are two walled gardens, two watered meadows and two orchards .. For viewing apply to the Owner, Mr Samuel Whiteway, Maltster ..'[9]

The mill was to remain in Whiteway ownership for many years. In September 1858 Samuel and his family had to escape from the burning mill house, which was gutted by the fire. Belt drives in the mill were destroyed and so were 100 bushels of wheat.[10]

Following this fire major rebuilding took place. In 1860 a new 20ft by 3ft 6in high breastshot waterwheel, carrying 'I. HALL' on its shrouds, was installed. Ivor Hall was an Ideford blacksmith (and, it seems, millwright). The wheel may have been cast for him by an Exeter ironfounder[11] – possibly Bodley or Parkin. Samuel's son John ran the mill from 1869. In 1893 the business was recorded as John Whiteway & Son, Millers (water and gas power), farmers, corn factors and manure merchants.[12] They advertised for a miller:
'Wanted a steady active young man as Miller; a good opportunity for one who has some knowledge of the trade to improve – Apply Whiteway & Sons, Town Mills, Chudleigh.'[13]

John's son William Samuel Whiteway was in charge by 1912; in poor health, aged 53 in 1923, he let the business to Francis Hamlin, a Tiverton man who had been running mills at Ashburton. William Whiteway and his father John both died in 1926; William's widow Bessie was now the owner.

William's eldest son, Samuel joined Francis Hamlin in the business in 1934. Hamlin & Whiteway Ltd ran a milling business from Quay

Town Mills with its leat and a second leat to Parkway Mill. From the Ordnance Survey map of 1905

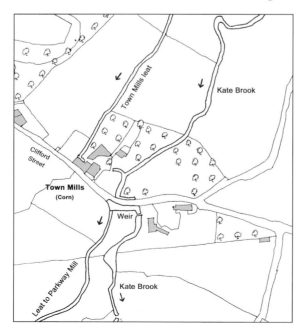

Town Mills, Chudleigh. Stone floor, with three of the four pairs of stones in shot. *Chudleigh History Group*

Town Mills now converted but with its 20ft diameter pitchback waterwheel still in place in April 2014

Penstock with water control gearing at end of launder, above the waterwheel, September 1994

Mills, Teign Road, Newton Abbot and milling ceased at Town Mills in 1939. In that year Bessie Whiteway died and Town Mills passed to Samuel, but the property was requisitioned by the Ministry of Food as a warehouse. [14]

A further disastrous fire in January 1941 rendered the Cornish family, who were living in the millhouse and running Town Mills farm, homeless. The roof and the upper floor of the mill were damaged in the fire. [15]

Town Mills opened as a craft centre in November 1972, £150,000 having been spent on restoration. [16] In 1985 Dorothea Restorations of Bristol restored the waterwheel for £16,000. [17] Two years later the mill was given Listed Building status. The craft centre closed in 1994 and the mill site was under redevelopment in 2004. Now a residential complex, the waterwheel survives. According to Martin Watts the cast iron gearing and bridging is of very high quality and of a design not seen elsewhere in Devon. [18]

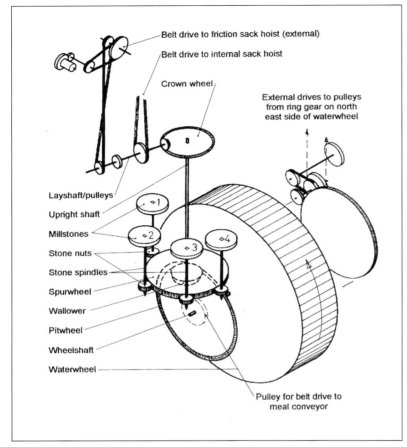

Belt drive to friction sack hoist (external)
Belt drive to internal sack hoist
Crown wheel
External drives to pulleys from ring gear on north east side of waterwheel
Layshaft/pulleys
Upright shaft
Millstones
Stone nuts
Stone spindles
Spurwheel
Wallower
Pitwheel
Wheelshaft
Waterwheel
Pulley for belt drive to meal conveyor

Town Mill, Chudleigh. The drive to the stones and additional drive via a ring gear to machinery in a separate building. Town Mills had four pairs of stones. Millstone pairs 1 and 2 were used for producing flour and were French burr. Pair 3 were composition and pair 4 were Peak. Pairs 3 and 4 were used for general milling and for animal feed.
The pitwheel was over 11ft dia. with about 160 teeth of $2\,^5/_8$ inch pitch. It was originally cast to fit a wooden waterwheel shaft. The wallower was a cast-iron bevel gear with 57 teeth. The spurwheel was cast in two halves and carries 168 cogs at 2 inch pitch. The stone nuts each were of 24 teeth. The split-cast bevel crownwheel was equipped with 130 cogs at 2½ inch pitch.
A ring gear or spur gear was bolted to the far side of the waterwheel. It was made up of five cast-iron segments with a total of 190 teeth. A pinion engaged with this gear, and its drive took auxiliary power to an outbuilding to the north of the mill via two sets of pulleys and belts.
Drawing by Martin Watts, following a survey in June 2003

Town Mill, Chudleigh. The drive to the stones. Pit wheel, wallower, great spur wheel and one of the stone nuts. *Chudleigh History Group*

Waddon Barton, Chudleigh
SX 8848 7962

In 1817 the 190-acre estate of Waddons belonged to Christopher Hellyer and included a lime kiln, limestone quarries and a threshing machine worked by water. [1]

A farm building remains on site today. It was once powered by a waterwheel, which was an overshot type, of about 18 or 20ft diameter. Water was piped and carried on two stone piers from the millpond to the launder. The Ordnance Survey map for 1888 confirms this – it shows an aqueduct or launder leading to the waterwheel. [2]

The structure has more recently served as a lumber store and the wheel and remaining machinery have decayed. [3] The mill barn was powered by the nearby Waddon Spring. Its machinery was probably only run for a couple of hours at a time, to grind animal feed, and ceased work before 1939.

Mill barn, Waddon Barton. The launder was on the far side of the structure, powering an overshot waterwheel

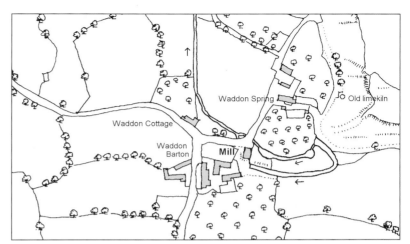

The mill barn at Waddon Barton was powered by an overshot waterwheel, fed by a launder and pipe from Waddon Spring. From the Ordnance Survey map of 1888

Harcombe Mills, Chudleigh

SX 8881 8158 – possible location
(Mill Meadow - tithe map, item 149)

There were watermills at Harcombe in the late seventeenth century;[1] a fulling mill was extant in 1729.[2] In 1742 mills in Harcombe and Brookesmore were referred to.[3]

William Williams of Exeter purchased lands and mills at Harcombe, previously the property of Thomas Clarke of Chudleigh, in 1745.[4] The later history of these mills is unknown; they may have disappeared when the ponds on the Harcombe House estate were created. These were on the Kate Brook. Harcombe House was built for Sir Channing Wills, a surgeon, in 1912.[5]

Farley Mill, Chudleigh

SX 8536 8096

Situated by the Teign, a plan of the mill and existing and proposed leats, dating from 1820, appear to indicate it was originally powered by the river.[1] Possibly the weir had been destroyed in a flood and it had been intended to build a new weir upstream. The waterwheel – or wheels – of this mill would have been undershot. A notice in the press in 1835 indicates Farley Mill had recently been rebuilt:

'To be Let, and may be entered on immediately, a set of New Built Mills, desirably situated adjoining the river Teign at Chudleigh, with twelve acres of Land and every necessary Building for a respectable Trade.
For particulars apply to Mr John Floud, Chudleigh.'

However the new mill did not receive its water from the Teign. A longer leat was cut from a

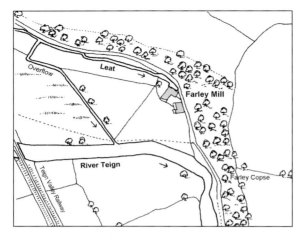

tributary, the Bramble Brook, with the head weir at SX 8506 8129. [2]

In 1845 a further advertisement appeared. The land – 12 acres in 1835 and 11 acres in 1845 – roughly tallies:
'To Millers. To be Let .. Flour and Grist Mills called Farley Mills .. situate about one mile and a half from Chudleigh .. in the immediate vicinity of good gristing, and in an excellent corn country, with a convenient dwelling-house, stables, outhouses, sheds and about 11 acres of meadow land and orchard, adjoining ..' [3]

A succession of millers worked Farley: John Floud, (a maltster), circa 1823-1841; William Leach 1851 and William Greenslade 1856. John Greenslade was miller in 1857; Samuel Ball was resident in the years 1861-1866 – he was then miller at Parkway Mill from about 1869 to 1881 or so. William H. Coombe was here in 1869, then John Putt in 1870 and Joseph Putt in 1878. John Putt was recorded as miller in 1881, working the mill with his son John, 24, born in Dartington: the Putts were here 1883 and in 1897, but in practice had ceased commercial milling in 1895 and John Putt junior used the premises as part of

Farley Farm until 1906 or so. [4]

The mill was for sale in 1918 when it formed part of the Haldon estate. It had remained so for at least eighty years: Sir Lawrence Palk had been listed as owner in 1838. [5] After the war the mill building was converted to a residence; the leat is no more than a shallow dry ditch today. [6]

Hyner Mill, Hennock
SX 8363 8163

This site was known as Hynor Mills when offered for sale in 1785. On occasions it was also recorded as 'Hiner Mill'. In that year the property became part of the extended Haldon estate owned by the Palk family. [1] Advertised as Haynor Mill in 1806, the building was to let:
'.. with a meadow thereto belonging, containing together 1a 10p, situate in the parish of Hennock, now in the occupation of Mr N. Ball or his under tenant, whose term .. expires at lady-day next, together with that dwelling-house, two orchards, and a garden adjoining the said mill ..' [2]
The Ball family were millers here later in the century – Nicholas Ball, born at Hennock in 1820, was at the mill in 1851; William Ball from at least 1857 until 1871 or later; John Ball in 1889. Lewis Pike was here in 1897 [3] but was in financial difficulties the following year.[4] Apparently the mill was used at the end of the century for grinding micaceous or shiny ore, mined locally. [5]

The site is near Hennock Bridge, between Hennock village and the Teign. Walls of the mill survive in a wood but are in a ruinous state. On the opposite side of the lane, uphill towards Hennock, was the Hennock Lead Mine, served by a higher, but parallel leat. These leats were supplied with water from the Beadon Brook.

Hennock Silver Lead Mine, Hennock

SX 8353 8154

Also known as Wheal Hennock, South Exmouth

In 1812 Sir Lawrence Palk of Haldon House granted John Gullett of Exeter a lease with licence to mine for ores including tin and lead on his estates in Hennock parish.[1] No serious mining developed until 1836 when an adit was driven and shafts sunk by a company headed by Colonel Drake, J. G. Maxwell and John Wise; Wise was a banker in Totnes.[2] A 36ft diameter waterwheel was installed to drain the workings. Almost 80 tons of manganese had been produced by 1838.[3]

The Hennock & Christow Mining Company was being run by Henry Molyneaux, the secretary, in 1841. He was based in Liverpool and was trading in manganese.[4]

About 1850 a wheelpit was constructed for a new waterwheel.[5] In April 1851 a vein of lead was cut through.[6] The mine was re-opened in 1852 following the installation of a 50in cylinder steam pumping engine constructed by Mathews, a Tavistock ironfounder. It was estimated to generate 105 horse power. A crushing engine was also erected. The chairman of the new concern was R. S. Gard and the mine agent was Captain Henry James. The lode being worked ran north-south[7] and by February 1853 the engine shaft had been sunk to four fathoms below the 50 fathom level. On the 30 fathom level five hundredweight of lead ore was being mined per fathom. 29 tons of ore were sold that year.[8] Timber, iron, coal and other mine materials were being supplied by Exeter merchants.

Despite the optimism displayed in the local press in 1852[9] the mine machinery was for sale in 1855:

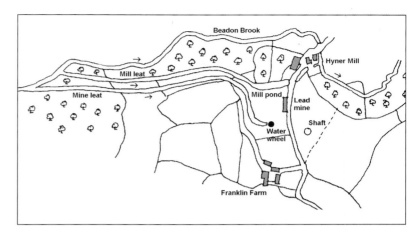

'The machinery consists of a 50-inch cylinder steam engine, with boiler, &c., complete; capstan and shears .. about 70 fathom of pumps; two water wheels and a crusher complete; kibbles .. horse whim, &c. The above mine is situated about half a mile south of Wheal Exmouth, and on the very same productive lode, and is held under a lease from Sir L. V. Palk, Bart., dated 22nd September, 1849, at 1-15th dues.'[10]

Following the default of a purchaser, a re-sale was advertised in October that year:
'.. all that very valuable sett, known as the HENNOCK SILVER LEAD MINE, together with a quantity of Mining Materials: comprising a thirty-eight feet water-wheel, 4 feet 6 inches breast, oak axles, iron sockets and cast-iron cylindrical ends; also a water-wheel, 18 feet diameter, 4 feet breast; drum and pinion wheel; crusher with perpendicular shaft, wheel, roller, and griddle complete; L. bob; 250 fathoms of 9-16 proof chain; zinc air pipes; pump rods; forty-feet shears .. At the same time and place will be offered for Sale a fifty-inch cylinder Pumping Engine, eight feet stroke, with twelve ton boiler ..'[11]

The parallel leats to Hyner Mill and Hennock Silver Lead Mine, taken from the Beadon Brook. From the Hennock tithe map of 1840. (after Schmitz)

It is not clear whether mining was continued here: a weighbridge at a Hennock mine was in a dilapidated state in 1863. [12] In 1862 South Exmouth Mine had been developed by Captain Nicholls on what is thought to be the same sett. [13] By 1864 Nicholls was managing the very successful nearby Frank Mills sett in conjunction with the Hennock mine. [14] Operations had ceased at Hennock by the end of 1867 and the mine was abandoned. At that time the mine equipment included smaller waterwheels than those used in earlier workings. A sale included a 20ft waterwheel, 18in breast and an 8ft wheel, 11in breast, together with *'tram irons, and waggons, kibbles ..'* [15]

Great Rock Mine, Hennock

SX 818 816

Iron mines at Hennock were being worked before 1850 but the cost of transporting the ore to the nearest port – presumably Teignmouth – for shipping to South Wales for smelting, made the enterprise uncompetitive and from 1860 until the arrival of the Teign Valley railway there was little development. [1]

Great Rock was worked from the mid-nineteenth century but it was only in the twentieth century that it was fully developed. It was the last metal mine in the county and was worked continuously from 1902 to 1969, initially under the management of the Ferrubron Co, who gave the mine the

Great Rock dressing floors in 1902.
Courtesy Devon Heritage Services, image 1578/7975A

Waterwheel by drying sheds in 1961.
J. Hamilton/Tony Brooks collection

name by which it is known today. A launder from Beadon pond, fed by the Beadon Brook, powered the waterwheels on site. These drove the mine machinery such as the compressor, washing plant and the elevator in the ore drying shed until about 1930 when an oil engine was installed. It was used to work the compressor. A water turbine then made the waterwheels redundant; the compressor was later powered by a diesel engine and after the Second World War most of the equipment was electrically powered.

The waterwheel powering the drying shed plant was still in situ in 1961. Part of the launder to take water to the drying-sheds waterwheel was still standing in 2002. It should be noted that all the workings are on private land and access is only granted with the permission of the owners. [2]

Pool Mill, Hennock

SX 805 822
Also known as Tottiford Mill

The mill has gone. It may well have been an old site as it stood just inside the parish boundary with Bovey Tracey and may have, in part, defined it at this point. It was probably demolished when the Trenchford reservoir was constructed in the 1850s. The reservoir was constructed to supply drinking water to the growing town of Torquay; in 1857 an iron pipe was to be laid to the town from Tottiford Mill. [1]

Earlier, in 1841, Edward Stone was miller. [2] In 1842, the property was to let. It appears to have formed part of the estate owned by the Palk family of Haldon House:
'Pool Mill, otherwise Toddiford Mill, Hennock .. Grist and Flour Mills .. together with a Bunt and Smut machine .. 2 pair of stones, a good Dwelling House, and all necessary outbuildings .. late in

Great Rock Mine. Washing plant water wheel. Photo taken before 1916.
Tony Brooks/Copyright Tucker collection

the occupation of Mr Stone, deceased .. term of 37 years from February last, annual rent £10 per annum ..' [3]

William Stone was listed as miller in 1850. [4]

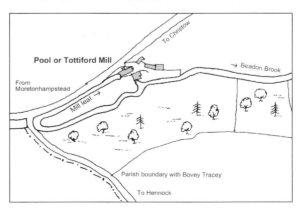

Pool Mill, Hennock, from a plan dated 1855. Not to scale

Moorbarn, Moor Barton, Moretonhampstead

SX 7878 8388

A site standing above the Trenchford Stream, thought to be on the Moor Barton estate. Moor Barton with 300 acres was acquired by Lawrence Palk in 1795 from John Stephens, a Moreton soap boiler. [1]

In 1980 Tom Greeves recorded a rectangular mill structure of granite with a wheelpit at this location. The wheelpit was about 26ft long by 3ft 9in wide. The waterwheel was powered by a spring-fed pond, which was partly stone lined. His assessment was that the structure was used for agricultural purposes. [2]

Frank Mills mine. Possibly the course of the leat to the dressing floors, seen in 2011.
Robin Stott, Geograph

Thomas Wills farmed Moor Barton in 1839 and 1878. In 2003 a seven-acre segment of the estate appeared on the market valued at £620,000 – the house had long since been demolished – and there was a reference to converted mill barns in woods. [3]

Frank Mills mine, Christow

SX 836 820

Frank Mills was a lead and silver mine in the Teign valley. Together with a second mine – Wheal Exmouth – it was developed on land owned by Edward Pellew, the third Viscount Exmouth, in the period 1852-1855. [1]

At 60 fathoms below ground a rich vein of lead, three feet wide, was discovered in November 1855. [2] In 1856 – Schmitz states in 1859 – dressing floors were established and a leat was cut to bring water from a small tributary of the Teign to power a waterwheel. [3]

By 1864 the mine was producing about 1,000 tons of lead ore a year. Captain Joseph P. Nicholls, the mine agent for both mines, born in Newton St Cyres in circa 1816, claimed that a railway in the Teign valley would reduce his transport costs by £800 per annum. Nicholls died in February 1869, aged 54. [4]

In 1876 Francis Dingey, a Truro ironfounder, presented a petition to the Vice-Warden of the Stanneries for the winding up of the mine. [5] D. W. Bain of Portreath was the proprietor of both Frank Mills and Wheal Exmouth when their machinery was advertised for auction in 1880. At Frank Mills the plant included:
'.. *pumping engine 60 inch cylinder, 10 foot stroke, with 2 boilers (12 and 10 tons), balance bob, shears, 2 sheaves .. 1 steam condensing engine, 25 inch cylinder, 5 feet stroke, with 10 ton boiler, fly wheel complete; crusher complete; 1*

steam crushing engine, 22 inch cylinder, 3 foot stroke, with boiler and fly wheel complete .. 25 foot water wheel, 2 foot breast; 8-head Stamps, with iron axle, heads, lifters and frames .. Bartle's pulveriser; 12 ft water wheels for driving buddles, with iron work .. several fathoms of launders and stands ..' [6]

Today the main features of the mine are the large barren waste tips. The remains of two engine houses, one probably housing the 25in winding engine and 22in crusher engine, were extant in the 1990s. That for the 60in cylinder pumping engine, which was supplied by the Perran Foundry, Cornwall, in 1854, remained in 1979. The main shaft, now no longer visible, at 1,050 feet, was the deepest in the valley. [7]

Shuttamoor Mine, Christow
SX 823 828

This was a small micaceous iron oxide mine on the boundary of Christow parish. Exploration began here in 1856. [1] By 1890 a mine shaft was marked as 'Old Shaft' on the Ordnance Survey map. A plan of the mine made at the turn of the century shows a waterwheel to the north of the eastern adit and in line with this shaft. E. M. Slatter worked Shuttamoor from 1897 to 1902 when Ferrubron took over the workings.

A second waterwheel was housed in the washing and stamping shed, roofed in corrugated iron. It powered a set of Californian stamps [2] and was fed by the small stream that rises to the north of Moor Barton, Moretonhampstead.

In 1910 the funeral of Elias Tucker, aged 65, was held at Hennock, following an accident here. [3] The following year the mine closed. The site is now largely hidden in a conifer plantation. [4]

Shuttamoor Mine dressing floor with stamps and overshot waterwheel, circa 1900. *Courtesy Devon Heritage Services. Chapman collection, image 1578/7975A*

Wheal Exmouth, Christow
SX 838 829

A silver-lead mine worked in conjunction with Wheal Adams, and Christow and Bridford mines in the 1850s, but which had been active from about 1810. In 1852 Messrs May and Bidwill had expended £10,000 a year in managing these mines. In August that year it was reported that 151 tons of silver-lead ore had been sampled and sold at £10 a ton. In May-June 1853 no less than 125 tons of lead ore had been dressed at Wheal Exmouth. [1] Harvey & Co of Hayle developed an engine specification for the Wheal Exmouth and Adams United Mines in 1853, [2] but it was J. E. Mare of the Plymouth Foundry who manufactured the 70in pumping engine, erected to work Porter's Shaft, in that year. [3]

The main plant at Wheal Exmouth was for sale in 1862 and included the pumping engine and several waterwheels:
'One 70-inch cylinder pumping engine, 12 ft stroke, equal beam, with two boilers of 12 tons each, furnished new to the company. One 22-inch whim engine, nine feet stroke .. One 22-inch horizontal stamping engine .. One 22-inch crusher engine .. One steam capstan ..Water wheel 40 ft dia, 2 ft breast, with axle and 12 stamp heads. Water wheel 20 ft dia, 18 in breast, with several smaller wheels ..' [4]

The 70in engine went to Wheal Neptune, Perranuthnoe in that year and was later purchased by Harvey & Co. It was moved to Prestongrange Colliery, near Edinburgh in 1874, where it has been preserved. [5]

D. W. Bain of Portreath held the mining rights in 1880, when there was a further sale of equipment including an 18ft iron waterwheel, 18in breast; possibly the mine had been worked on a smaller scale after 1862 or the spoil heaps were re-worked. [6]

The mine was visible from Canonteign House, the country seat of the local landowners, the Exmouth family. The engine house for the 70in engine has survived, now a private house. It and the nearby round and octagonal stacks were built with ornamental features to improve the view from the house; the mine was later screened with trees. [7]

Ashton Mills, Ashton
SX 8424 8428

This is the first mill site on the Teign upstream from Farley, in Chudleigh parish. Mills were noted at Ashton in 1720. [1]

In 1785 Nicholas Pearse, a Crediton miller, insured *'.. his house and Water Corn Mill adjoining with the going gear therein and Materials thereunto belonging situate at Ashton in Devon, in his own tenure £80. Bakehouse, stable and Pigsties all adjoining near £20. All stone cob and thatched.'* [2]

The mills were leased in 1800 [3] and by 1804 were being run by W. Walker (or Waller), an Exeter ironmonger. A second mill, an iron-mill, had been built nearby, powered by the same leat:
'Wanted, One good Hammerman, One good Reaping Hook Finisher, Two good Shovell Finishers, and Four good Horse Nailers ..' [4]

The enterprise was unsuccessful and Walker/Waller was declared bankrupt in 1807. The sale notice provides useful detail:
'Ashton Mills, Devon. To be Sold, by order of the assignees of William Waller, a bankrupt, for the residue of a term of 21 years, commencing .. September 1803, subject to the clear yearly rent of £35 .. All those Mills called Ashton Mills, situate within the parish and manor of Ashton .. lately built at the expense of upwards of £2,500 consisting of an iron-mill, worked by a water wheel, 12 feet in diameter, with a balling furnace, two tilt hammers, one for making iron, the other steel, a blast for making iron, with two single bellows and two smith's bellows, all blown by a waterwheel, and every other requisite for carrying on the business of iron-making.
Also, a Dwelling-House with a GRIST MILL

*comprising two pair of mill-stones, and with about
Five Acres of Garden and Meadow Land.
The purchaser may have immediate possession of
the iron mill, but the dwelling-house and grist
mills, with about an acre and a half of land, are
let for three years .. at the rent of £20 per annum.
The premises.. are well-supplied with water,
having the advantage of the whole stream of the
river Teign ..'* [5]

A further auction was attempted in 1808 but no
more is known of the iron mill.

By 1835 William Marks, a native of South
Tawton, was running the grain mill. In July that
year one of his daughters was assaulted twice on
her way home from visiting her sister there. Her
assailant, Thomas Penrington, was a beer house
keeper. The way was dark – it was evening and a
thunderstorm with lightning raged above. Her way
involved crossing a ford on the Teign. Penrington
was later apprehended but escaped from his
premises while the constables were drinking his
beer below. [6]

By 1851 Marks was 65 and his son Joseph, 24,
was assisting him. [7] It is possible that the iron mill
survived in some form as this sale notice from
1861 is suggestive:
*'Clearance Sale. Ashton Mills, Ashton. .. Auction ..
the undermentioned effects, the property of
J. W. Treby, Esq. (lately worked by the Baraytes
[sic] Company), comprising about eleven tons of
ground baraytes in barrels, about seven tons of raw
ditto in bags and hutch; twenty empty barrels, ..'* [8]

In 1866 the entire Ashton estate was for sale –
about 1,000 acres, and fourteen farms, Ashton
Mills and two public houses were included. *'Mr
Lewis Langworthy, the Bailiff at Canonteign, will
show the estate'*, which indicates the property had

Ashton Mill with low breastshot waterwheel by Stenner and Gunn of Tiverton, seen in August 1986. The wheel was said to have been installed in 1934, as a replacement for a 16ft by 4ft 6in timber wheel. The mill was converted in 1991. *Alan Stoyel*

Ashton Mill: pit gear with line shaft drive from pit wheel, August 1986. The pit wheel has been recorded as of 8ft diameter, with 104 teeth at 3in pitch. In recent years only a single pair of French burr millstones survived. *Alan Stoyel*

35

formed part of the Exmouth family holdings. [9] R. Pitts milled here in 1871. The Howard family moved in in 1901. William Howard was milling in the period 1910–1919. In 1911 he was operating as a coal merchant, miller and farmer. He had previously worked at Broken Hill, New South Wales and in Paraguay, presumably as a miner. Ashton Mill adjoined a coal yard which was once served by the Teign Valley branch line. By 1927 only one pair of stones was in use, for animal feed, but the wheel also provided lighting for the house and farm buildings. [10] Stanley Howard still ran the mill occasionally in the early 1970s.

The mill is now a private house, converted in 1991 and Listed Grade II. It is said to be eighteenth century, possibly earlier, with nineteenth-century alterations. [11] The low breastshot waterwheel was manufactured by Stenner and Gunn of Tiverton in the twentieth century and was said to have been installed in 1934, replacing an earlier, timber, wheel, recorded as 16ft by 4ft 6in with 15in floats in 1927. The leat from the Teign is still in water. In 2008 a bypass channel from the leat was cut around the waterwheel and a second-hand turbine installed downstream from it.

At **Place Barton**, also known as Lower Barton, SX 854 846, the Great Barn survives, now with a thatched roof. It may have been the barn in a watercolour by John White Abbott in 1826, which shows a tailrace issuing beneath it. An *'excellent thrashing machine'* was advertised here in 1855, but without reference to water power. [12]

Christow Mill, Christow
SX 8343 8506

This was always a grain mill; one was said to have functioned here in the sixteenth century. It formed part of the Palk family estates from early in the nineteenth century until sold in 1867. [1] John Pinwill was miller from at least 1839 until 1867. Pinwill came from Teignmouth but his wife Martha was a local lass. In 1851 Henry Thorne,

Ashton Mill leat, mill cottage and mill, August 1986.
Alan Stoyel

Ashton Mill: stone floor with octagonal tun and grain feed, August 1986.
Alan Stoyel

Old millstone at Christow Mill

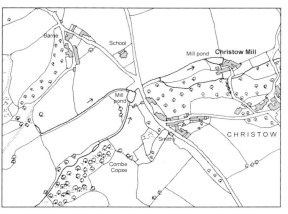

Christow Mill was powered by water from two streams which fed two mill ponds. From the Ordnance Survey map, 1888

from Great Torrington, was living in his household, employed as miller. [2]

By 1870 John Northcott was butcher and miller. A native of Torbryan, aged 30 in 1871, he employed his brother-in-law John Trebilcock, born in Ashton in about 1820, as miller. [3]

Northcott, or possibly his son of the same name, was advertising for a butcher to work at Christow in 1901 and was still listed as miller in 1919. [4] Fred Cousens had moved in by the autumn of 1921 and continued in the meat trade as well as that of miller. [5]

The mill was for sale in 1925; the sale notice was the first to provide some detail:
'Auction .. Freehold Properties known as Christow Mills and Higher Great Meadow. Lot 1. – The Mill is a four-storied building, with 2 Pairs of Stones and Dynamo, driven by powerful overshot wheel etc, Registered Slaughter House, Outhouses and Stabling, Piggeries, Shippens and Sheds, with Pasture Field .. Dwelling House .. A lucrative Wholesale and Retail Butcher's and Miller's Business has been carried on for a great number of years .. The tithes are apportioned at

Mill pond at Christow Mill; a low retaining wall is visible under the trees on the right. The pond is up to four feet deep. The 22ft by 2ft 6in waterwheel with iron shaft, cast-iron shrouds, timber arms and buckets, is now partly buried following collapse of a section of the wheelpit wall. [9]

£1 16s 1d. ..To View apply on the Premises ..' [6]
Cousens was still listed as miller in 1926. Milling may have ceased by the start of the Second World War.

The remains of the cast-iron waterwheel were still in situ in 2001 when the property was for sale, having been converted and incorporated into the mill house in 1982. [7] In 2013 potter Abi Higgins was resident here. [8] The waterwheel was powered by the Shippen Brook, which fed two millponds above the mill.

Teign Valley Barytes Mine, Bridford

Previously Bridford Consols

SX 830 865

In 1847 the search was on for the northern end of the great lead lode that was about to be exploited further south, notably at Frank Mills, Christow. Open-cast workings were begun with little reward and in 1850 the mine became known as Bridford Consols. [1] An engine shaft was sunk and a 40in cylinder steam engine was erected, designed by Hocking and Loam of Cornwall, to pump out the workings. This was set to work in July 1853 but only small quantities of lead ore were recovered. The adventurers noted large masses of barytes in the workings, estimated at no less than 100,000 tons, [2] and this ore later became the focus of operations.

The Teign Valley Lead & Baryte Mining Company (Limited) was formed in 1870; one of the four directors was Sir Lawrence Palk, Bart, MP. [3] In 1875 the company re-opened the old Bridford Consols workings. It appears water power was available on site to grind the barytes but to achieve the purest quality the ore had to be carted to Exeter at a significant cost, for processing at a mill near Exeter Quay, which resulted in restricted sales. The Teign Valley railway was used from 1882 and separate sidings laid in at Teign House. Eventually the ore went to Exeter via the shorter Longdown route after the line was extended in 1903. [4]

In 1883 the sett was owned by Gidley and Harris of Exeter. Military engineers demolished the chimney and engine house housing the steam engine as an exercise in 1884. [5] By 1891 the barytes mine foreman, Joseph Rundle, from Tywardreath, Cornwall, was living in Venn Mine Cottage. Rundle was still supervising operations ten years later. He had previously lived in Burnley, Lancashire. [6] The Devonshire Baryta Company bought the sett in 1927 and radically improved operations by the Second World War, installing new machinery and raising output to 800 tons per week. By 1958, when the mine closed, 400,000 tons of barytes ore had been recovered. The site was sold off in 1966. [7]

A leat from the Rookery Brook provided water for the steam engine, and for the washing plant, and a waterwheel, said to generate 10 horsepower. An undated plan which shows the engine house and would thus appear to have been made before 1884, when it was demolished, shows the ruins of a water mill at the east end of the surface workings. This possibly pre-dated the lead mine, Bridford Consols. Barytes was used in the production of barium carbonate, chloride and peroxide. [8]

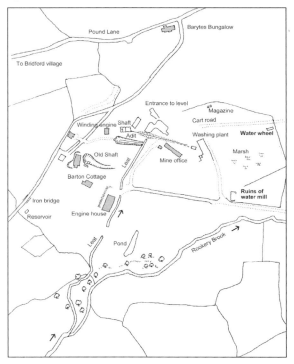

A copy of an undated plan of the Bridford Barytes Mine but made before modernisation of the site. In addition to the shafts, adit, washing plant, winding engine and engine house, the sett included a remote waterwheel and the ruins of a separate water mill. *From DHC plan 6347-0*

Stone, Bridford

SX 8275 8614

Waterpower existed here in 1888: the Ordnance Survey map shows an 'aqueduct' or launder taking water from the Rookery Brook to the farm. This indicates that the elevated leat was used to power an overshot waterwheel. Confirmation comes in an advertisement published in spring 1895:

'.. Auction .. Stock Farm, known as Stone, now in the occupation of Mr Knapman, whose tenancy will expire at Michaelmas next .. Dwelling-house .. 71 Acres of Meadow, Pasture and Orchard Land and Coppices, now let at a rental of £71 15s per annum. The Land Tax on it amounts to 17s 4d per annum. The purchaser will have to take at a valuation .. a water wheel, launder, threshing machine, cider press, engine, horse wheel and driving gear for same ..' Two months later the farm was offered to let on a yearly tenancy. [1]

H. Knapman was the tenant in 1897 and William Creed in 1901. [2] By 1920 the waterwheel had become redundant:

'.. Also will be Sold .. Iron-Framed Water Wheel, 14ft diameter, with Gear attached, in very good condition; Threshing Machine, complete with shakers; single-screw Cider Press and Vat; Apple Engine, Horse Wheel and Gear attached, on Stone Farm, Bridford .. For viewing please apply to Mr Bennett, Manager, Scatter Rock Macadams Ltd, The Grange, Bridford.' [3]

Stone Mill, Bridford

SX 8248 8613

George Dormer was miller and owner of Stone Mill in 1840. He may have milled here in 1851, but the census returns indicate that he stayed – on occasions, at least, with his brother-in-law, William Langdon, of Stratton, Christow. [1]

Stone Mill was over a mile from Bridford village, down a narrow lane, but high up above the Teign valley. Rookery Brook supplied the water power. This was the nearest mill to the village and provided its bread as the 1866 sale notice indicates:

'Bridford. For Sale .. all that Freehold Grist Mill with two pair of Stones, Machinery and a never failing supply of Water, Dwelling-House, Outbuildings and about 1½ acre of Garden and Orchard called Stone Mills. There is also a Bakehouse attached, and a very profitable business has been carried on in both trades for several years past by the present owner. For viewing and for particulars apply to Mr Geo. F. Dormer on the Premises.' [2]

Anne Pike was tenant, together with her sons Joseph, 20, and William, 17. She ran the mill with Joseph in 1871. William worked the bakehouse. [3] They stayed until about 1889 when the property was again on the market:

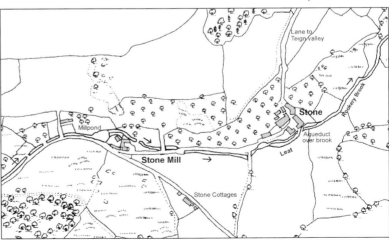

Stone Mill and Stone Farm, Bridford. Both were water-powered in 1888. From the Ordnance Survey map

'.. The mill is in capital working order and there are two pairs of stones. There is also a large Baking Oven, recently built, and a good sound business is done in both .. the Flour and Smut Machines will be included with the Mill ..' [4]

William Pitts, from Hennock, was baker and miller in 1891, assisted by William Perkins and apprentice George Holman. [5] A major fire in 1893 reduced the buildings to ruins:
'.. the dwelling house, mills, bakehouse, and the whole of the contents were entirely destroyed, and the inmates barely escaped in their nightclothes . [The domestic servant girl, rescued by the

postman, later died] .. the origin of the fire, it appears, was in the bakehouse, but in what way it occurred is impossible to explain. Mr Pitts is only partially insured, and the loss will be severely felt by him ..' [6]

Stone Mill appears to have been rebuilt as George Counter, a baker, was here in 1906. He damaged his hand working a thrashing machine. [7] It was still standing in 1922 when *'Percy Johnson, working at Stone Mills, Bridford, fell into fly wheel [possibly of a traction engine] and was cut to pieces.'* [8]
By 2013 only ruined walls remained on site.

Bridford Mills, Bridford
SX 8351 8701

This was the next water-powered site on the Teign, upstream from Ashton Mills. Its leat ran to the west of the river and west of Bridford Bridge.

Bridford Mills in 2013. The waterwheel (or wheels) was internal, probably low breastshot or undershot.

Today this part of Bridford parish is known as Bridfordmills. There was a mill here in the eighteenth century. It was included in marriage settlement in 1753 [1] and in 1780 Thomas Saunders, a Chudleigh millwright insured the property; a grain mill:
'.. On his house, Millhouse, Mills, one Water Wheel, Two pairs of Stones with going gears therein Stable and cellar adjoining in the parish of Bridford in Devon, in the tenure of Thomas Mortimer, Stone cob and thatched £100.'
The waterwheel was internal, possibly a low breastshot; the mill was sketched by the Reverend John Swete in February 1794. [2]

John Smallridge (or Smalridge) was miller and tenant in the years 1825-1833. The mill was to let in 1825:
'.. for a Term of 7 Years,.. all those Valuable Flour Mills, with three pair of excellent Burr Stones, and Bolting Mill; together with a Dwelling-House .. Meadow .. and two Orchards ..' [3] Rebuilding had taken place since 1780 as the mill was now operating with three pairs of stones. In 1827 the estate was for sale and now included the

small farm of Ramsey, with 22 acres. [4] Smallridge died near Newton Abbot in 1836, aged 78. [5]

Elias Cornish of Ashton was the owner from at least 1833 until 1840, and probably 1841 when once again the mill was for sale. Edmund Stooke had taken over the tenancy by 1839. [6] A further tenant was sought in 1850 when it was being operated by Branscombe and Woodbridge and was producing 80 to 120 sacks of flour a week. [7]

William Surridge, born in Silverton in about 1823, worked the mill with his brother John, 20, in 1851. On census night they had a visitor, millwright Thomas Creed. [8] The brothers were still here in 1889:
'Wanted a Married Man as a Waggoner - Apply Surridge Bros, Bridford Mills, Dunsford.' [9]

In 1891 William Surridge had retired to Teign Vale Cottage. On census night he was living there with his wife Elizabeth, son John, a miller, another son Frederick William, a domestic servant and William Pugsley, a visitor and evangelist/preacher, a native of Bow. Bridford mill house appeared unoccupied at this time. [10]

By 1901 Frederick was running the mill and employing Joseph Holwill, 44, as carter. Frederick's brother John, now 44, had retired. On census night Frederick's household included Peter Child, a gospel preacher from Surrey. [11] Frederick was still here in 1921:
'Wanted, Young Lad to help in Mill, milk cow or two and make himself generally useful – Surridge, Bridford Mills, Dunsford.' [12] He died in 1957.

There is a chapel near Bridford Mills. It may have been erected by the Surridge family; preachers staying with them in both 1891 and 1901 suggest that they were ardent non-

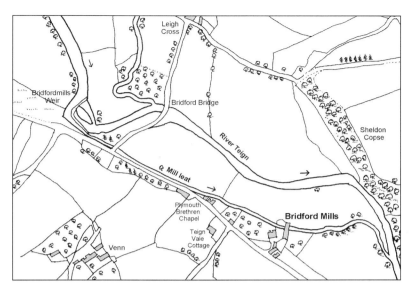

conformists. In 1927 an Armfield turbine was at work, generating 23hp on a head of 8ft 9in, possibly less. It powered a roller plant flour mill. Equipment also included kibbling, crushing and mixing machines and a chaff cutter, a cleaner and a 24in dia. saw. [13] Today the much altered mill stands within the Teign Valley Nursery estate. The leat is still in water.

Bridford Mills in 1794, sketched by Rev. Swete. *Courtesy Devon Heritage Services, image reference 564M/F5/153*

Bridford Mills in 1888. Powered by a leat from a major weir on the Teign. The Plymouth Brethren Chapel to the north west of the mill was probably associated with the Surridge family, here from at least 1851 to 1921 or later. Teign Vale Cottage was also associated with the family. The neighbourhood was known as Bridfordmills, which might imply the mill had at one time been equipped with more than one waterwheel

Pond near Many Waters, seen from the footpath linking Neadon Lane and Pound Lane. Spring 2014

Right: the chimney stack that has survived at Birch Aller Mine. The brick upper section has gone

Birch Aller Mine, Bridford

SX 826 869

A silver-lead mine which was active in the 1850s. It was described at the time as:
'.. about one mile north of Wheal Exmouth .. on the same .. lode ..' In the grounds of Many Waters, a private house, a chimney stack survives, restored by the Dartmoor National Park Authority and the house's owners in 1995. The remains of the engine house which housed the 30in cylinder steam engine, were incorporated into a rock garden, still extant in 1980. [1]

The engine shaft was being sunk in April 1851 and 'A steam engine is about to be erected ..' It had reached a depth of 30 fathoms by June 1852 'and the lode opened upon at that depth ..' [2]

This was an unsuccessful venture as the sett and the entire mine's plant were for sale by auction in the summer and autumn of 1855:
'.. all that very valuable Sett known as the Birch Aller Silver Lead Mine, together with a quantity of Mining Materials: comprising a 30 feet water-wheel, 3 feet breast, balance bob, shears, horse whim, 8-arm capstan, whim machine, proof chain, pulleys and stands, pump rods, kibbles, tram waggon, kieves, shieves, and brasses, a quantity of iron .. At the same time and place will be offered for Sale a 30 inch Pumping Engine, eight-feet stroke in cylinder and six feet in shaft, with eight ton boiler ..' [3]

The 30-foot waterwheel may have been powered by streams running into a man-made pond near Many Waters, which survives today at SX 8266 8696 and which can be seen from a public footpath which runs between Neadon Lane and Pound Lane. It was possibly used to operate a set of stamps.

Sowton Mill, Dunsford

SX 8251 8832

Listed Grade II, English Heritage ID: 1214794

The mill may date from 1580. *'Indenture 16 October 22 Elizabeth. Grant by Richard Champernowne of Modbury to Nicholas Sparke of Dunsford, in consideration of £4 of right to make a weir in the river of Tenye upon the river water and lands of the said Richard containing by estimation twelve perches .. limited by certain marked stones .. within the parish of Bridford .. for the conveying of a watercourse to a mille to be built by the said Nicholas upon landes called Wynscombe in .. Dunsford .. paying twenty pence yearly ..'*

Winscombe Farm today stands on the hill near Sowton Mill. So the weir, leat and mill referred to are clearly Sowton. [1] John Williams was miller in 1757. [2]

In 1796 Sowton was to let. It was then part of the estates belonging to the Palk family of Haldon House:

'All that compact and desirable Barton and Farm commonly known by the name of Sowton Barton, Winscombe and Sowton Mills, situate in the parishes of Dunsford and Doddiscombsleigh, now in the possession of Mr. William Collins, as tenant thereof, .. adjoining the turnpike road leading from Exeter to Moretonhampstead. Consisting of a good farm-house, barns, stables, linhays, pound-house, and other necessary outbuildings; also a good set of water grist mills adjoining the river Teing [sic], about 33 acres of rich watered meadow, 9 acres of orchard; 3 acres of coppice wood .. and about 305 acres of

Iron ring – with double start pockets – and arms for a low breastshot waterwheel, seen in 1993. Note the opening in the mill wall on the right. This may have provided for a second waterwheel shaft. There were two waterwheels originally, probably en echelon. Granite stonework provides for two narrow channels and a bypass, but this may date from the installation of a small turbine downstream: the channels appear too narrow to sustain waterwheels of any power. Nevertheless the waterwheels here had a single set of arms, as at Fingle Mill, upstream. When Alan Stoyel visited in 1960, a complete waterwheel was still in situ

Sowton Mill and the leat from the Teign, on a garden open day, May 1993

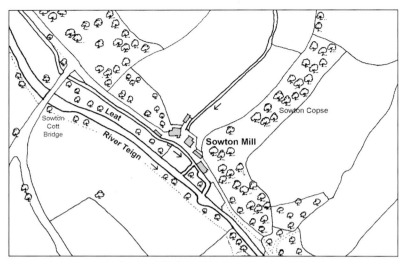

Sowton Mill, the mill leat, and the river Teign.
From the Ordnance Survey map of 1888

At the mill the leat now runs through three channels separated by granite walls. A water turbine had been installed here although the ring of a low-breastshot waterwheel remain. There were originally two waterwheels.

When W. H. Worth visited in 1927 and again in 1934 he recorded the surviving wheel as 13ft 6in by 11¼ in. It was short of water in the summer. A second waterwheel was 23in breast, but had gone by 1927. Equipment then included a 30in circular saw, bruiser, chaff cutter and a pair of stones, together with two pairs of disused stones. Flour had not been made since 1885. [11]

The mill was for sale again in 1945 *'..with Water Wheel and exceptional water power .. About 27½ acres ..'* [12]

A turbine was installed in 1950. In 1986 a replacement – an Ossberger crossflow turbine with a 13ft head, rated at 30kW – was introduced a few yards downstream. The leat is now also used to power an Archimedean screw turbine upstream. This was commissioned in autumn 2013. [13]

very good pasture, tillage and furze ground .. with a good limekiln thereon ..' [3]

In the nineteenth century this was known as 'Chaffe's Mill'. It belonged to Sir L. V. Palk in 1837. In 1841 Roger Chaffe, 65, milled here with his son George, 30, who had been born at Dunsford. George ran the mill in 1851 and farmed seven acres. [4] He was here in 1872 when he appealed for information concerning a black mare colt *'stolen or strayed from the premises ..'* [5] Following his death in 1874 his son John Chaffe ran the mill. He was selling cider at four pence a gallon in 1895. [6]

The mill was to let in 1899 with 18 acres of land. [7] Mark Smallridge milled here in the years 1901-1908. [8] By 1918 the Commercial Union Assurance Company owned part of the Haldon estate and Sowton Mill was sold for £1,275 to Mr Graham. [9] F. G. German was miller in 1919. [10]

The Archimedean screw turbine powered by the mill leat – running through the vegetation seen in the foreground – and sited just above Sowton Cott Bridge. The installation was commissioned in the autumn of 2013

Wheal Lawrence, Dunsford
SX 813 884

This was intended as a copper mine, located on the south bank of the Teign, east from Steps Bridge, on land owned by Sir Lawrence Palk of Haldon House. Some lead ore may have been raised in 1851 but otherwise the enterprise was notably unsuccessful. Considerable funds were spent in constructing a leat over two miles long from a weir on the Teign some way above Steps Bridge, and then conducting the leat water via launders across the river, not once, but apparently twice. A large waterwheel on the north bank was used to drain both Wheal Anna Maria and Wheal Lawrence. The mines were worked separately until 1853 when they became a single concern. The leat water that was aqueducted to the south bank suggests that further waterwheels were erected or were planned to be installed to operate stamps and dressing floors. In 1853 steam engines were introduced. [1]

Wheal Anna Maria, Dunsford
SX 807 883

First known as Dunsford Mine, the sett was leased by Baldwin Fulford of Fulford House in 1847. This was intended to be a copper mine. Development was slow and involved bringing a leat from a weir on the Teign a mile and a half above Steps Bridge, then known as Dunsford Bridge or Dunsford New Bridge. [1]

Mine agent Henry James, 46, a native of Calstock, was lodging at the now vanished Half Moon Inn, near Steps Bridge, on census night 1851. Ten years earlier he was agent for a mine in Hennock and by 1861 he had moved back to Cornwall, employed as a captain at a Redruth mine. [2]

The leat served this mine on the north bank and also Wheal Lawrence, on the south bank, on lands owned by Sir Lawrence Palk of Haldon House. *'Whereas a Leat or Watercourse has been lately made and constructed from the left bank of the river Teign about a mile and a half above Dunsford Bridge in lands of the said Baldwin Fulford and thence along the said left side of the said river for about a mile and thence across the said river by an Aquaduct [sic] as now erected to lands of the said Sir Lawrence Vaughan Palk and Lawrence Palk and thence along the right side of the said river to a Water Wheel now erected about a quarter of a mile below Dunsford Bridge and from thence across the said river by an Aquaduct as now erected to a meadow to that point of the mill stream running at the head of the said meadow which adjoins the gate leading into the Turnpike Road above the building used as an Iron Foundry.'* [3]

The description of the route of the watercourse is less than clear and a plan of the sett, if such exists, would help in understanding the sites of the waterwheels on both setts. A public footpath in Dunsford Wood follows the course of the mine leat, roughly on the 80m contour, which may have provided a launder perhaps 30 foot clear above the Moreton road at the mine site.

By 1850 a large 32ft by 6ft waterwheel was at work at Wheal Anna Maria, draining both mines by means of 120 feet of flat rods. Disputes over the percentage of money to be paid by the adventurers on Wheal Lawrence for water charges led to closure and operations were restarted in 1853 by which time steam engines had been put to work and the two setts brought under one management team. [4] The mine was unsuccessful and it is doubtful if any useful quantities of either lead or copper ore were raised. A closure date is not known, but it was probably before 1858.

Dunsford Mills, Dunsford

SX 8101 8863

This was a grain mill on the Fulford estate, powered by a leat from the Teign. The Hemmens family were tenants from at least 1779 to 1805. In 1779 Thomas Hemmens insured the dwelling house and mill and its machinery for £250; *'furniture and trade'* for a further £100. The buildings were stated to be of cob, roofed with thatch, although the ground floor of the mill was probably built of stone to enable the wheelpit(s), and cog pits to be formed. In 1799 he paid £2 2s 2d rent to the Fulford estate.[1] Having taken on John Norrish as an apprentice in 1800, he was a bankrupt in 1803.[2] Undeterred by this setback he insured the mill again in 1805, this time for £300 with a further £200 on the waterwheel and machinery.[3]

Dunsford Mills by the Exeter-Moretonhampstead road. The stone-lined leat is on the right, in shadow. It ran under the building in the centre and powered two waterwheels in 1857, driving six pairs of stones. July 2014

Joseph Phillips was miller from at least 1818 until his death in 1839, aged 67.[4] John Phillips ran the business in 1851, employing four men at the mill and a further labourer on his farm of 16 acres. His son John, 19, no doubt was one of those who assisted him.[5] The mill used to be reached from the south bank of the river by a footbridge but this was destroyed in 1856.[6]

It was clear from a sale notice published in the following year that the mill had been rebuilt since 1779:
'.. Auction .. all those desirable Flour and Grist Mills known by the name of Dunsford Mills, which comprise a good Dwelling House and Offices. The Mills .. consist of six pair of Stones, Dressing Mill, Flour Mill and Smut Machines, with two Water Wheels, Hutches and Lofts, which will contain 5,000 Bushels of Wheat .. Pound-house, five-stall Stable, Workshops, Waggon and Cart Sheds, Gig-house, an excellent Piggery .. Meadow, Orchard and Garden Land .. The Mills have been for many years in the occupation of Mr Phillips and his family who have carried on a most extensive business ..'[7]
This must have been one of the largest grain mills on the river, with two waterwheels and six pairs of stones. Flour was traded beyond the parish.

A butcher, John Connett of 35 Fish Street Hill, London, purchased a 1,000-year lease on the property for £2,650 in February 1858.[8] A further sale was announced in 1880; the estate now included a six-stall stable and a new cottage.[9] John Hellier was the owner in 1881; he advertised for a *'.. Young Man as Second Miller or Improver ..'* and two years later, Hellier, who advertised his role as *'Auctioneer and Law Agent'*, was seeking a tenant.[10] One tenant was J. Chaffe, possibly from Sowton mill.[11] In 1901 the mill may have been worked by Francis Connett, 27, Joseph Hellier's nephew, and probably a relative of John

Connett. Joseph Hellier lived nearby and was listed in the census as auctioneer, surveyor, farmer, cattle dealer and miller. Living with him was Richard Penhale, a baker. [12] He quit the bakery at Dunsford Mills in 1902. [13] In that year Hellier won the contract to supply the workhouse run by Exeter Corporation of the Poor, with flour at 19s a sack. [14] Walter John Hellier was mill owner in 1903. He sought *a Man to drive miller's waggon and make himself generally useful indoors; good wages; must be trustworthy and steady'*. Francis John Connett was his foreman miller in 1912. [15] Joseph Hellier junior took over the business in 1930. [16]

In December 1926 the internal waterwheels were respectively 15ft by 5ft 6in and 14ft by 4ft, both with iron floats 14in long. Three of the four pairs of stones could be worked at once. The wheels were generating 8.25hp but could produce 16hp with a higher flow. All the millstones were 4ft 6in diameter. The leat was, until recently, still 'live'. [17] The mill has now been converted into a number of residential units and the wheels and machinery have been removed.

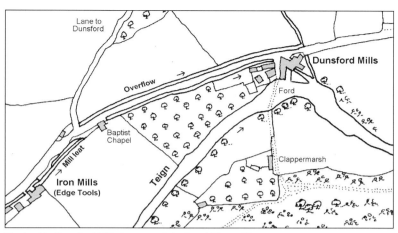

The leat to Dunsford Mill also served the Iron Mills and began at a weir just upstream from Steps Bridge

Stepping stones across the Teign; these give access to Dunsford Mills from the south bank. There was a ford here in the nineteenth century

Iron Mills, Dunsford

SX 8072 8845

English Heritage ID: 1288508

The undershot waterwheel at Iron Mills is visible from the road near Steps Bridge. It was powered by a leat from the Teign which also turned the waterwheels at Dunsford Mills. It was out of use in 1937 but had been restored by 1992. In the nineteenth century – and early in the twentieth – it powered two tilt hammers, later powered by electricity.

An iron forge on this site may have existed from the late eighteenth century; tool-making may date from the year the waterwheel was installed. The mill building is of random granite walling with tile and corrugated-iron roofing. It is thought to date from the early nineteenth century. [1]

Thomas Helson leased the property from Baldwin Fulford in 1837 and was running the business with his son Thomas in 1841. The enumerator recorded Helson as 'cutler' but he was otherwise known as an edge tool maker. [2] His products were similar to those fashioned at the Finch Foundry at Sticklepath, now in the hands of the National Trust.

Helson, aged 69 in 1851, was then employing three men and a boy. All the employees lived in the Helson household. By 1861 his son, Thomas

The Teign in its wooded valley above Steps Bridge. The weir directed Teign water into the leat which powered both the Iron Mills and Dunsford Mills.

junior, had taken over the running of the forge, with his son John, 16, and four other workers; his father having retired. [3]

By 1891 John Helson was an ironmonger of Fore Street, Exeter; he was alerted after a fire had gained a hold in the mill on one October night. He reached the mill four hours later. Two fire brigades were then able to control the flames before they spread to the dwelling house, but £300 damage was estimated to the mill machinery. [4] Next May the premises were to let:

'To Edge Tool Makers, Machinists ..To be Let, with immediate possession the Iron Mills, Dunsford ..where a good edge tool business has been carried on for a number of years. There is a good dwelling-house, garden, an extensive workshop .. with powerful water-wheel driven by a never-failing stream. Necessary machinery will be erected to suit any trade ..' [5]

Samuel Chudley, who had been a child apprentice in 1861, was tenant and edge tool maker here in 1901. He worked the forge with his son Joseph, 20. [6] Mr Loder followed but gave up in 1931, dogged by ill health. [7]

W. H. Worth recorded the waterwheel as 14ft by 4ft 3in, developing 6hp or so; 8hp with full flow in the leat. In February 1932 there was not enough power to work the grindstone, which needed to run at 530rpm. The waterwheel was then turning at 14rpm. A 20hp Ruston Hornsby oil engine provided standby power. [8]

Since 1931 the business has been run by the Morris family. They bought the mill in 1981, after a brief closure. Their products are worked from Sheffield carbon steel. Bill hooks are made for hedge-layers and other tools are forged for thatchers, all made to order. Work includes plating and planishing. [9] One of the old tilt hammers survives, now electrically driven, together with an electrically-powered drop hammer. [10]

Right: the low breastshot waterwheel at Iron Mills. It had been in a derelict state until restored by Ron Hobley of Broadclyst in the late 1980s. It powered two tilt hammers until 1937. The large cast iron naves are by W. C. Bodley, Exeter

The Teign from Dunsford to Chagford

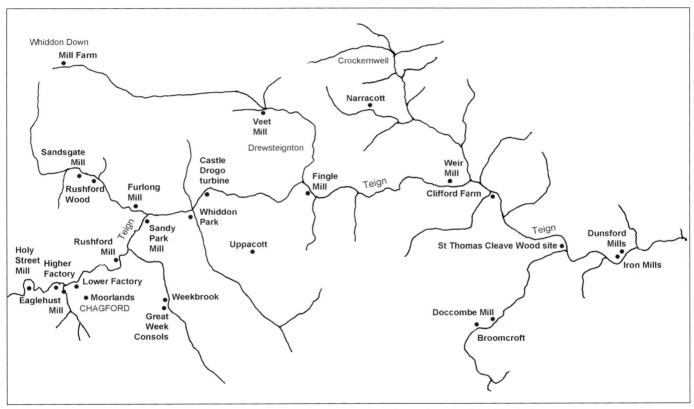

The river flows down from left to right, from Chagford to Dunsford. Sites include farm mills, woollen mills, hydro-power plants, a saw mill and a mine, as well as a number of grain mills. Listings run upstream

Doccombe Mill, Moretonhampstead

SX 7800 8699. Also known as Dockham Mill

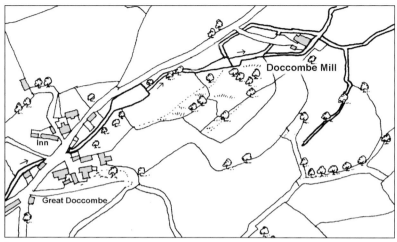

Doccombe Mill, sited below the village. The stream was small, so two millponds provided the power to the waterwheel. By 1905, when the mill was shown as disused, these had silted up.
It is possible that the upper pond was later utilised by the owners of Broomcroft.
From the 1885 Ordnance Survey map

Streams from Mardon Down in the north west and Blackingstone in the south east converge above Great Doccombe. The combined stream then changes direction, running for nearly two miles to the north east before joining the Teign by Dunsford Wood. It powered the grain mill at Doccombe, which in 1825 was run by William Guscott. [1]

The mill was owned by the Dean and Chapter of Canterbury in 1839 when William Hamlyn was tenant. The property included a pond and orchard.[2] Hamlyn had married Ann Wrayford, daughter of Samuel, a farmer of Stacombe, below Mardon Down in 1832. Their two sons were born at Doccombe in 1855 and 1857. In 1858 the family emigrated to St John's, Newfoundland, where the parents' third son was born in 1861; [3] the property was advertised to let:
'All those desirable Flour and Grist Mills .. lately in the occupation of Mr William Hamlyn .. about 2 miles from Moreton on the Exeter road ..' [4]

George Cole, a local man, milled here in 1861. [5] He was probably succeeded by Samuel Vicary, a native of Bondleigh, who had a desperate time at Doccombe. His son, aged between four and five was crushed to death by the upsetting of a cart being loaded with furze near his own residence. The cart was being loaded by Vicary himself. The jury returned a verdict of *'Accidental death'*. [6]

In 1877 Vicary was charged with stealing 200 feet of oak plank and several pieces of wood, the property of William Looney, from Leigh farm in November 1876:
'On 6 November, the defendant's house was searched .. and the marked planks were found there ..' [7]

The mill had ceased to work by the beginning of the twentieth century. The mill house survives, though considerably rebuilt, and is thought to date from the seventeenth century. The mill building has now gone and it is thought some of the machinery found its way to Sticklepath. [8]

Just upstream a bungalow called **Broomcroft** was for sale in 1944 with a water wheel in the garden. [At SX 778 869] [9]

Mill site, Thomas Cleave Wood, Moretonhampstead

SX 796 886

The site of a watermill, possibly extant in the eighteenth century, exists on the edge of Moretonhampstead parish, at the foot of St Thomas Cleave Wood. It was at work in 1639. The signs of a mill and a leat which cut off a loop of the Teign are evident in this remote spot, by the river's south bank. [1]

Clifford Farm, Moretonhampstead

SX 7807 8968

The farm was owned by the Earl of Devon and later by Lord Hambleden. The mill formed part of Lord Hambleden's estate which came onto the market in November 1828, following his death. [1] The mill building stands near the farm and by a lane to Moreton; it has been converted to a private residence. An undated sectional plan in the Heritage Centre shows the fall of a leat through Coppice Wood and Withy Bed, Ley Field and Orchard, to a waterwheel of 20ft diameter. The wheel was powered by a stream that rises on Mardon Down and from springs at Little Woolston and flows north to join the Teign just below Clifford Bridge. [2]

Weir Mill, Drewsteignton

SX 7724 8990

Also known as Wear, Were and Ware Mills

Powered by a leat from the river Teign and extant in the seventeenth century. [1] In 1799 it was auctioned:
'To be Sold .. Wear-Mill Tenement .. Drewsteignton, consisting of a Mill-house, with three Pair of Mill-Stones, a Dwelling-house, Stable, Sheep-pen, hogstyes .. a Courtlage, and about 18 Acres of Orchard, Meadow, Arable and Waste Land; now in the occupation of William Lambert Gorwyn, subject to a Lease for a Term of 99 years ..' [2]

The three pairs of millstones suggest this was a mill with more than one waterwheel at that date. From 1824 William Hamlyn was miller. [3] An arson attack destroyed the mill in 1833. It then formed part of the Wallon estate:
'£50 Reward. Whereas Weir Mill, in the parish of Drewsteignton, was on Friday evening last ..

Is this Weir Mill? 'Mill on the Teign', a drawing by W. Spreat, circa 1850. A small mill with, it appears, a low breastshot waterwheel at each end of the building. Weir Mill was known to be small and have two waterwheels, with water channels either side of the building. This image is a probable candidate.
Royal Albert Memorial Museum, Exeter

Destroyed by Fire, an Investigation having taken place .. by the Magistrates of the District, it was the unanimous opinion the premises were destroyed by an incendiary. The above reward will be given by Mr Lambert of Wallon, on the conviction of any Person who may be implicated in so atrocious an offence ...' [4]

Hamlyn remained at Weir Mill after the fire: his daughter Thirza was born here in 1836 and her brother Henry in 1838. She later emigrated to New South Wales, Australia. Hamlyn moved to Hittesleigh Mill. [5] William Lambert owned and occupied Wallon, Weir and Little Shilstone in 1840. His tenant at Weir Mill was Thomas Bull. [6] Bull was miller when the premises were offered to let for a term of 7½ years in September 1841. [7] William Phillips, a local, was here in 1850 and ran the mill with his son George in 1861. They farmed the land too. When William retired

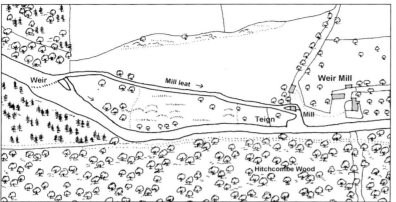

Weir Mill, with a leat from the Teign, 1885. The leat is about 430 yards long and today a dam across it, near the weir, restricts the flow to the mill site. From the Ordnance Survey map. The mill was also indicated on Benjamin Donn's 'A Map of the County of Devon' in 1765

George took over. He left in 1887. [8]

The mill that had been rebuilt after the fire in 1833 was a small structure: it was to let in 1890: *'.. Freehold Property called Weir Mill .. adjoining 'Wallon' .. 25 Acres ..   Cottage .. stone and slated shed for three cows, stabling for three horses, barn, linhay and pigstye and a small stone and slated grist mill with water wheel and excellent water power .. Land tax 12s 6d, and head rent to Lord Devon 4s a year, payable in respect to Weir Pool. Tenant Mr John Strong, who quits at Christmas.'* [9]

The estate was sold to Mr Knapman for £3,610 [10] In 1897 it was to let again: *'Drewsteignton. To be Let .. farm known as 'Wallon and Weir Mill' .. in the occupation of Mr W. W. Rowland as tenant .. good Homestead, .. and about 147 acres .. on the banks of the river Teign .. The taker will have the free use of the threshing machine, mill, apple engine and cider press on the farm, belonging to the landlord.'* [11]

The mill was disused by 1901. W. H. Worth noted that there had been three waterwheels here – one 10ft 6in by 3ft 6in. On the other side of the mill he thought there had been two – 11ft 6in by 22in and 11ft 6in by 3ft. But there were only two wheels;

the last mentioned was actually the by-pass channel. All had gone by December 1926. [12] Internally the mill footprint is about 24ft by 16ft.

The low-breastshot wheels powered millstones via treble gearing, with possibly two pairs of stones on the left side of the building, looking upstream. [13] Although the waterwheels had gone, some of the wooden machinery, which was probably new following the 1833 fire, survived in 1941 when seen and photographed by Donald Muggeridge. It has the look of an eighteenth-century millwright's work, with its face and lantern gears. But the small Dartmoor communities in the nineteenth century possibly did not need and maybe could not afford modern cast and wrought iron machinery [14] It was a ruin in 2002: *'Weir Mill is beautifully situated .. within the National Park .. The Teign forms a spectacular boundary, feeding the .. mill leat which flows past the ruins of the old mill ..'* [15]

Narracott and Lower Budbrook, Drewsteignton
SX 7560 9150

On a small stream to the south of Crockernwell which, with others, flowed south to merge with the Teign above Clifford Bridge. In 1889 the following farms were advertised: *'Auction .. All that conveniently situated and productive Freehold Estate known as Narracott and Higher and Lower Budbrook .. about 319 acres .. residence, cowhouses, pound house and cellar, stable, barn, finishing and chaff cutting rooms, granary, first class machinery, driven by a powerful water wheel well supplied with water .. in the occupation of Mr William Strong ..'* [1] This waterwheel site was probably at Narracott. A second notice, posted in 1924, offered the estate for sale; but the waterwheel had been supplemented by an oil engine. [2]

Fingle Mill, Moretonhampstead

SX 7456 8975

A weir on the Teign to the west diverted water to the mills, which stood downstream from Fingle Bridge. A grain mill and a fulling mill existed here in 1639. These were almost certainly both fulling mills in the mid-eighteenth century, when owned by Sir William Courtenay and run by members of the Ponsford family, some of whom were wool-combers. [1] George Ponsford leased the mills from the Earl of Devon in 1780; his sub-tenant then was John Brely. [2]

The tenant in 1782 was John Cadlick Davy, a Crediton merchant. He insured, in addition to his Crediton residence: *'Millhouse, two Fulling Mills, Water Wheels and Materials at Fingle in the parish of Moretonhampstead in Devon in his own tenure Stone cob timbered and thatched £50. Utensils and stock and Goods in Trust or on Commission therein £40.'* [3]

A survey of his Moretonhampstead estates was made for the Earl of Devon in about 1790. At that time the two mills were described as Fingle Mill and East Fingle. East Fingle was the fulling mill and Fingle Mill had been converted to a grist mill. George Ponsford was the tenant, [4] but he almost certainly sublet to the Brely family who had a long association with the grist mill, the last member of the family, Henry Charles Brely, dying here in 1890. The fulling mill had probably ceased work by 1810 or 1815.

John Brely junior was miller, aged 72, in 1851. His son Henry was in charge into the late 1860s. [5] John's eldest daughter Ann had married George Lambert Gorwyn – probably related to the owners of Wallon and Weir Mill, Drewsteignton (q.v.) – in 1840. Their son John Lambert Gorwyn, Henry's nephew, was miller from about 1870

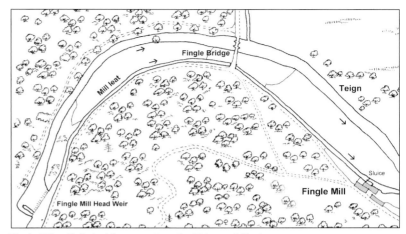

Fingle Mill, with its leat from a weir on the Teign and Fingle Bridge to the north west. The second mill here appears to have been under the one roof. From the 1885 Ordnance Survey map.

Fingle Mill with its leat and undershot waterwheel at some date before the 1894 fire. The waterwheel is narrow with just a single set of arms for the paddles. The roof of the building nearest the camera is of thatch. *Alan Stoyel collection*

53

until about 1890. [6] William Parr moved in but the mill was burnt down in July 1894. Parr later ran Gunstone Mills, near Crediton. The last water-wheel here was cast for millwrights Dicker of Chagford; both naves survive in the wheelpit. The waterwheels here were each capable of driving a pair of fulling stocks or a single pair of millstones. Old photographs show a narrow low-breastshot wheel, its paddles secured to a single set of arms. When the two mills were functioning it appears the waterwheels were overlapping on plan, partly alongside one another. [7]

The surviving waterwheel at Fingle Mill in about 1880. It was 11ft 9in dia. by 1ft 7in breast, with floats of 1ft 5in. A second identical wheel once worked alongside. What appears to be the by-pass channel can be seen in the foreground, right. The mill's roof appears to be of thatch. As Martin Watts notes, these narrow waterwheels seem to hark back to a late-medieval tradition of millwrighting.
Stereoscopic Gems/Tom Greeves collection

The ruined mill in May 1987. The site of the low breastshot waterwheel, with the opening for the waterwheel axle. A possible opening for a second waterwheel is evident to the right. This suggests a configuration where two narrow waterwheels overlapped, en echelon, standing in separate water channels. The nave castings survive in the wheelpit and are designed for wooden shafts. *Alan Stoyel*

Castle Drogo Turbine House, Moretonhampstead

SX 7251 8987
Listed Grade II, English Heritage ID: 1396453

A weir across the Teign below Hunter's Tor, at SX 7227 8963, directs water to the Turbine House sited by the river's south bank. Sir Edwin Lutyens, who designed Castle Drogo, also designed this structure. Two Gilkes turbines, one of 75hp, the other rated at 35hp, were installed in the single-storey reinforced-concrete building in 1927. It originally carried a thatched roof but is now protected by corrugated metal.
Electricity cables reached Castle Drogo via a culvert under the Teign, and used to power a lift as well as provide lighting. A flood shortly after the Second World War resulted in the 220V supply being carried on an overhead cable. The power house continued in use into the 1990s although a mains supply reached the castle in the 1950s. The larger turbine, which had suffered damage, and its generator have been removed to Castle Drogo's stable block. The small turbine remains in situ. The turbine house now forms part of the National Trust's Castle Drogo estate. [1]

Veet Mill, Drewsteignton

SX 7357 9146

Veet Mill was in existence in the mid-seventeenth century. [1] In 1745 it was owned by Sir Coventry Carew who leased it together with Fox Hill to John Ponsford of Ford. [2] The Ponsford family later came to own it. [3] In 1826 William Bremridge appears to have been milling here and John Lewis occupied it in 1840. [4]

James Nickels, a local man, was the miller from at least 1850 – a year when there were three bakers in the village – until 1878, [5] when the property was to let:
'.. all that well frequented Inn with a Brew-house and all necessary outbuildings, called 'The New Inn' and a good pasture field contiguous thereto, containing half an acre or thereabouts, and also all that Mill with the dwelling-house, garden and meadow, belonging thereto, called 'Veet Mills'.. For viewing the properties application is to be made to Mr James Nickells, [sic] the tenant; and further particulars may be obtained from him; from the owner, John Ponsford, Esq, Ford, Drewsteignton ..' [6]
From at least 1871 Nickels – by then recorded as miller and innkeeper – had been running the New Inn in the village and late in 1877 had been charged with keeping his house open during prohibited hours. He was fined, following a previous conviction. By 1891 he had moved away to Woodbury, where he worked Exton Mills with his son Charles. [7]

In 1889 the Veet estate was offered to let as a farm. [8] But in 1894 the mill had been converted:
'To Coachbuilders & Wheelwrights. – For Sale, good dry Ash, Oak and Elm Plank, Wheel Stocks, very dry, and Oak Spokes. – Apply Smith & Son, Saw Mills, Drewsteignton.' [9] An appeal made in the following year identifies Veet as the location:

Veet Saw Mill in August 2013. The wheelpit survives to the left of the structure and would have housed an overshot waterwheel. The roof may originally have been of thatch

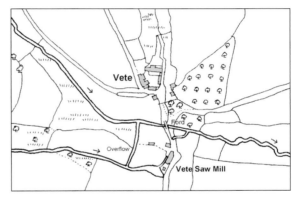

The saw mill at Veet, from the 1905 Ordnance Survey map. The cartographer has employed the alternative spelling 'Vete'. The leat ran round the contours from a weir below Ford House and was about a mile and a quarter long. It had been partly ploughed out by 1960

'Strayed from Veet Saw Mill, Drewsteignton, a Black Horse Pony; shod, white star on forehead, and one white hind foot. Also a young Bay Mare Cart Colt .. All reasonable expenses paid. – Smith & Shore, Drewsteignton.' [10]
The small mill building remains, now stripped of sawing machinery and is used as a sculptor's studio. It stands by the lane from Drewsteignton village to Veet Mill Farm and is thought to date from the seventeenth century. [11] On the far side of the mill is the silted-up wheelpit which at one time possibly housed a 20ft diameter overshot waterwheel. This was powered by a leat from a weir over a mile away at SX 722 918.

Mill Farm, Whiddon Down, Drewsteignton
SX 6950 9240

There was probably a mill by the farm in the seventeenth and eighteenth centuries, when it was just known as 'Mill' – in 1660 or so near 'Wheaton Down', now Whiddon Down. [1] It was still 'Mill' in 1871 when John Rowe, a local man, was farming here, but milling may have ceased 60 years earlier. [2] In 1893 the property was described as Mill Farm when the dwelling house, with a thatched roof, was destroyed by fire. The local press noted that there was a good stream of water at the bottom of the yard. [3] There was no knowledge of a mill building here according to the residents in 1998. [4]

Nearby, close to Drascombe Barton, a mine was being developed in the 1840s. Tin, copper and some silver were the ores reported. Bristol adventurers had sunk a shaft to a depth of 34 fathoms. Whether any water or steam power was established is unknown. The mine was known as **Drascombe** and was at SX 7012 9200. [5]

Uppacott, Moretonhampstead
SX 7337 8854

Uppacott was owned by the Earl of Devon in 1851 when a barn containing a thrashing machine and about 160 bushels of wheat, barley and oats, were destroyed by fire. A further fire occurred at Howton Farm, about a mile away. The local press declared this was the work of an arsonist – 'an incendiary'. [1]

Plans have survived for a new barn dating from 1857 and these included provision for a water-wheel, probably overshot, of about 20ft diameter. [2] The 1885 Ordnance Survey map shows a leat and

millpond running to the barn, above and across the lane to Clifford Bridge. [3] This is a surprisingly high location for a water-powered installation at 250m up, but the water was there to be used; an overflow from the leat was still 'live' in May 2005.

There was no mention of a waterwheel when the farm was to let in 1908. [4] The property formed part of Lord Hambleden's estate which came onto the market in November 1828, following his death. [5]

Whiddon Park, Chagford
SX 7214 8928

A leat, about 750 yards long, once ran to Mill Cottage just to the east of Whiddon Park House. This is probably where a waterwheel was working in 1897:
'Auction .. at Whiddon Park Farm House .. two superior fields of Corn, the property of Commander Evans RN .. there is a water-power thrashing machine on the property free to the purchaser .. The reed and straw can be all removed ..' [1]
In 1921 William Thorn of Forder Farm was paid damages caused by a leak to the leat which passed through his land to Edward Arthur Craig Fulton's estate at Whiddon Park. [2] Arthur Wilde, writing in the local press in 1944, of his walk from Fingle Bridge, gave the impression that the wheel was beyond the park:
'.. Leaving the gorge and the river [Teign] I made my way along a meadow-path and came upon an old water-wheel, which I believe still operates; and entering Whiddon Park I was soon admiring Whiddon Park House in its setting among the trees ..' [3]

At some stage the estate came into the hands of the Drewe family of Castle Drogo. [4]

Sandy Park Mill, Chagford

SX 7127 8927

William and Joseph Nickels purchased the leat to
Sandy Park from John Rowe of Easton, Chagford,
in December 1834. The leat was 851 feet long and
about five feet wide and ran to *'to a Mill thereon
lately erected, .. situate near the River Teign and
Doggermarsh Bridge ..'* [1]
This seems to imply that Sandy Park Mill was a
new construction in the nineteenth century. In
1835 Joseph Nickels, then a Bishopsteignton
miller, offered the property to let:
*'Chagford .. To be Let.. all that excellent Flour
and Grist Mill, called Sandy Park Mills, now in
the occupation of Mr Perring, comprising two pair
of the very best Stones, Bunt and Smut machines,
good Lofts and Hoisting Gear, with a never failing
stream of water from the River Teign .. situate in a
neighbourhood where the best of grain is grown ..
For particulars apply to Mr Nickels, Old Inn,
Sandy Park ..'* [2]
Nickels decided to dispose of the mill in 1850; it
was now fitted up with three pairs of stones:

Sandy Park, Chagford. In the left foreground is Sandy Park Mill, before rebuilding as the
Mill End Hotel. The road from Moretonhampstead to Whiddon Down crosses the Teign in
the foreground at Dogmarsh Bridge, to the right of the tall trees. The hamlet in mid
distance is Sandy Park. The view was probably taken before 1929.
Chapman and Son postcard, author's collection

The low breastshot waterwheel, by Dicker of Chagford, at
Sandy Park, surviving within the hotel complex in spring 1995.
Recorded in 1926 by W. H. Worth as a 16ft by 4ft 1in
breastshot, when it was said to generate about 15hp, supplying
electric light at 150V, 12amp. It had been worked up to 20hp

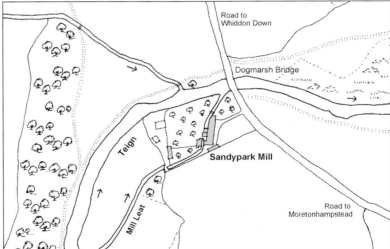

Sandy Park Mill. The leat was 850ft long from a weir on the Teign. Adapted from the
1905 Ordnance Survey map

'Freehold Mills for Sale .. consisting of one Dwelling House, Mill House, Water Grist Mill, 4-stall stable, Barn, Outhouses, Orchards, Gardens, and Premises, known as Sandy Park Mills, near Doggermarsh Bridge, on the Teign, in Chagford .. These well accustomed Mills, which have three pairs of stones, Bunt and Smut Machines .. and, having been lately most substantially built, are in good repair .. For viewing apply to Mr Joseph Nickels, the owner, on the Premises ..'[3]

The Nickels family continued to work the mill. In 1880 Henry Nickels advertised for help: 'Wanted a Miller, general hand, that understands stone dressing. Indoor preferred. Apply Hy.

Nickels, Sandy Park Mills, Chagford.'[4] The following year he was employing Daniel Frost as his waggoner and George See as his mill worker. Both lived with the family at the mill.[5]
Henry was also farming here and he probably retired in 1903 when he advertised the sale of sheep and bullocks, a sow in farrow, pigs, potatoes, mangold, turnips, cabbage, a rick of meadow hay, rick of clover hay and four ricks of oats.[6] His widow, Sarah J. Nickels, died aged 72 in 1908. She had lived at Sandy Park since her marriage.[7]

Walter William Bolt & Co were the last millers here: the last flour was produced in 1922.[8] In the 1930s the leat and waterwheel were used to generate electricity. The mill was initially a private residence but in 1929 was converted and extended to become the Mill End Hotel.[9] The low breastshot waterwheel, cast for mill-wrights Dicker of Chagford, is still in situ. The leat runs from a weir on the Teign at SX 7107 8904; its flow in 1934 was about 820 cuft per minute.[10]

Furlong Mill, Drewsteignton
SX 7094 8952

A farm mill on the White Water, a tributary of the Teign than flows in a generally southerly direction from Whiddon Down. A weir on the river, south of Furlong, ran south east, north east and then east to a millpond adjoining the mill barn. This water-powered site appears to have been active in 1869 and was advertised to let in 1876:
'Farm called Furlong .. with a dwelling house, and all requisite farm buildings, a water-powered threshing machine and corn mill, cider pound and apple engine and two labourers cottages and gardens .. may be viewed on application to Furlong House ..'[1]

The Mill End Hotel today. It has been enlarged from the nineteenth-century mill building extant in 1929.

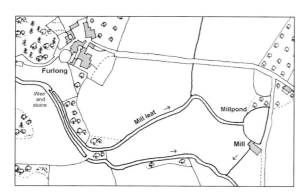

Furlong and Furlong Mill. The leat follows the contours eastwards from a weir on the White Water to the south of Furlong. From the 1905 Ordnance Survey map

It was offered to let again in 1880 and was on the market in 1903. [2] The stone-built barn had been converted to a private residence by 1995, just visible from a nearby lane. The waterwheel was saved by Bob Barron and re-erected at Albany House, Sticklepath, to generate electricity. [3]

Weekbrook Cottages, Chagford
SX 7162 8764

Near the junction of roads to Sandyways Cross and Drewston Cross by the entrance to a house is what looks like a large dolls house with an undershot waterwheel by its side. This may have been replaced by a turbine to generate electricity.

Great Week Consols, Chagford
SX 713 875 (Mine).
Also known as the Teign Valley Mine

By the steep bridleway towards Week Down can be seen a very deep gully leading down to the main tin openwork, about 50 feet deep. The bridleway runs by a leat which was still flowing in 2013. The 1905 Ordnance Survey map shows a tramway to the other side of the bridleway, probably worked as an inclined plane: it had a drum house at its head. William Ellis, the owner of Great Week, permitted development on the sett in 1886. [1] Charles Henry Maunder, from Stoke Climsland, in Cornwall, was mining agent, living in Westcott Cottage. [2] In 1887 a 40ft by 3ft waterwheel had been installed to pump the mine shaft, now 30 fathoms deep, where the tin lode had been found, running east-west. Water was pumped up to adit to enhance a stream running to the wheel, stamps and tin floor, now under farm buildings. Two buddles had been completed; three others were under construction, together with

finishing floors and a square buddle. A steam engine was being erected to power the stamps and winding operations. [3] The waterwheel drove a line of flat rods to pump the shaft with balance boxes to control its speed. [4] Output was 55 tons of black tin until 1892, then worth £3,367. Work was re-started in 1896 and up to 18 miners were employed until 1899. [5] Increased costs and a possible deterioration in the quality of the ore brought closure and the smith's plant and materials were auctioned off in April 1903. [6]

A **grist mill** *'fallen into decay'* stood in Weake, in the Manor of South Teign, in 1650. [7]

Rushford Wood tin workings, Chagford
SX 7024 9002

In the wood there is evidence of tin working from earlier centuries, including an openwork and tin streaming. Workings were on a north-south alignment, extending over about 300m. Documentary evidence dates activities to the 1440s. [1] The wood was then owned by the Knapman family, wealthy tin adventurers. [2] A surviving mill structure measures 7.4 by 4.0m internally and an open bearing stone for a waterwheel shaft survived in 1990. [3]

Sandsgate Mill, Chagford
SX 6989 9019

On the White Water, on the right bank. A small drystone structure, dating from the seventeenth century or earlier, has internal dimensions of approximately 4m by 3.5m. It was powered by an internal waterwheel: a culvert runs away from the mill in the south east corner. The site must have been a tin mill. [1]

Rushford Barton, Chagford

SX 7075 8902

A single reference to water power here appeared in a sale notice for 1868:

'Auction .. Live Stock, five-horse-power thrashing machine, cider press and apple engine, cast-iron water-wheel and machinery, horse power chaff cutter, dog cart and harness .. the property of Mr W. Hooper, quitting the Barton at Lady-day next .. horses, pigs .. a five-horse-power thrashing machine with shaker and blower by Dicker, a cast-iron water-wheel about 8 ½ feet diameter, and machinery driven therewith, a flour mill by Curson and Sons, corn bruiser by Ransom and Sons, and root pulper by Bently, and the driving gear, all lately new, an excellent cider-press and apple-engine with horse-wheel and chaff cutter and gear attached, good as new ..' [1]

The waterwheel was probably powered by a small stream that runs eastwards from Higher Withecombe.

Barn at Rushford Barton, seen from the lane to Sandy Park, July 2014

Rushford Mill, Chagford

SX 7062 8846

Local historian Jane Hayter-Hames has stated that Rushford Mill was in existence in the fifteenth century. [1] Ann Dicker ran the mill in 1792 and William Coombe in 1818. [2] In the mid-nineteenth century it formed part of the Rushford Estate, cantered on Rushford Barton. It was for sale in 1849:

'Auction .. Estate called Rushford Barton together with the Wood and Mills, situate in the parish of Chagford .. Farm House, and convenient outbuildings .. [322 acres of] .. Arable, Meadow and Pasture, Orchard and Woodland in the occupation of Mr. William Hooper. The Mills, on the River Teign, consist of a Dwelling House, Mill House and Machinery and [18 acres of] of Meadow and Pasture Land in the occupation of Mr Peter Tarr .. surrounded by beautiful and romantic scenery ..' [3]

Peter Tarr and his descendants were associated with Rushford Mill for much of the time from about 1829, when he employed a nine-year old apprentice, to 1935 when John Tarr left the mill. [4]

With the stepping stones crossing the Teign, the mill was a popular subject for postcard printers. A weir on the Teign at SX 6997 8820 fed a leat which ran about half a mile eastwards to the mill, where it turned a waterwheel within the building, thought to be a breastshot type.

Peter Tarr was still the miller in 1849-1850. The mill was included in a further sale in 1855:

'The Rushford Barton Estate .. offer for Sale .. farm-house .. in the occupation of Mr. William Hooper, a highly respectable tenant, at a very moderate rental of £250 per annum; also a corn mill driving three pair of stones, situate on the river Teign, with miller's house, and several enclosures of rich meadow land, in the occupation

Rushford Mill in 2014. The tailrace runs in culvert. The internal waterwheel was in the centre section of the mill

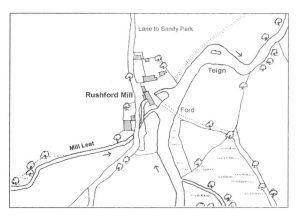

Rushford Mill in 1885. The leat is about half a mile long from a weir on the Teign

of Mr Coneam, at a rental of about £45 per annum.' The estate was purchased by the rector, Hayter George Hayter Hames, in 1856. [5]

By 1870 John Tarr was miller; [6] he had been born at the mill in 1829 and was to live here all his life. In 1881 he employed two men. Ten years later he divided his time between milling and farming, employing his 22-year-old son John junior as miller's assistant. [7] When John died in 1895 the press published a brief obituary:
'It was not only his integrity and uprightness of character that won him respect, but his kind and genial disposition was sufficient to endear to all with whom he came into contact.' [8]

Until 1935 his son used the water-power for threshing and milling for animal feed:
'To be Let .. the well-known and highly productive farm known as 'Rushford Mill', being a rich Sheep and Dairy Farm .. good farmhouse .. tea gardens, outbuildings, threshing machine and other machinery driven by water power and about 116 acres of very fertile land ..' [9] John Tarr junior died in 1936, the press noting that the family had been at the mill for generations. [10] When W. H. Worth visited he recorded the waterwheel as breastshot, 12ft by 3ft, with floats of 9½in. In 1926 it worked

three pairs of stones, a kibbler, a winnower and a chaff cutter. [11]
The wheel was in use until 1947 – it was repaired, with wood, in 1938, when G. C. Hayter Hames paid £5 3s 3d for timber and sawyer's work at Yeo Mill and five shillings for transport to Rushford. It was later broken up. [12]

At one time the leat supplied the nearby swimming pool. In very wet winters the road by the mill has flooded up to a depth of four feet. [13]

Rushford Mill in 1905.
Alan Stoyel collection

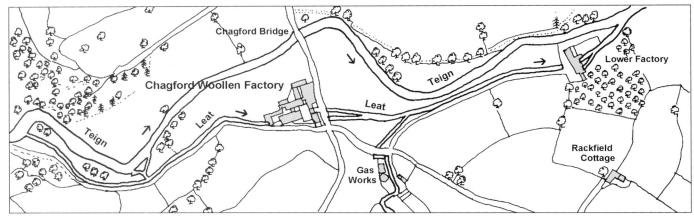

Chagford Woollen Factory – or Higher Factory – and the Lower Factory. They were both powered by a leat from a weir on the Teign just below Holy Street Mill. Both factories were disused by 1885, when the Ordnance Survey map for Chagford was published. The Higher Factory is now just ruined walls. Lower Factory has been converted to residential use. The leat is still 'live'. To the south of the gas works site is 'Millpond', originally Eaglehurst Mill

Woollen Mills, Chagford

Higher Factory/Factory Cross SX 6938 8783,
Lower Factory SX 6975 8791

Richard Berry, an Ashburton blanket and serge manufacturer, established large woollen mills here in 1800 or a little earlier – at Factory Cross, known as Higher Factory. [1] A fulling mill had previously existed nearby in 1327 [2] Weaving and spinning shops were based at Higher Factory. Lower Factory – also known as Blanket Factory or Down Factory – was operational by about 1820. A rack park adjoined it. Here fullers would have stretched fulled cloth on tenters. This factory was on the site of an earlier grain mill. [3] A leat from the Teign, with a weir just below Holy Street Mill, served both sites and is still maintained in water today.

Richard Berry died in 1828 [4] and his son John took on the business. In 1829 John Berry directly employed 115 men, 127 women and 98 juveniles. Many other outworkers were involved in the business. Long ells or serges were produced: blankets and miner's cloths. [5]

With the decline in trade caused by competition from Yorkshire and the introduction of cheap cottons, closure may have come about in 1848. [6] Worsted machinery was for sale in 1851. [7]

Fulford Vicary, related to a family of Newton Abbot tanners and a woollen manufacturer of North Tawton, took over the woollen mills and was involved in establishing a gas works at Chagford in 1869 to provide lighting for his new enterprise. [8] In 1867 he advertised for staff: *'Wanted, Workpeople and Power Loom Weavers at Chagford Factory. – Apply to Fulford Vicary, North Tawton; or to R. L. Berry, Esq, Chagford.'* Vicary also manufactured blankets and serges, having installed the power looms.. [9]

During the Franco-Prussian war in 1870 he was employing 140 or more staff, with large orders for blankets, but numbers declined and by 1874 only 55 or so hands were employed. [10] Closure of the new venture came in 1882 or a little earlier: *'To be Sold or Let by Tender, as from Michaelmas 1882 .. all those extensive factories now and for 15 years past in the occupation of John Fulford Vicary, Esq, as Woollen Manufactories, with two large iron water-wheels, each 14 feet in diameter and 13 feet and 13 feet*

1 inch respectively in breadth, worked from the River Teign. Also nine Cottages .. the whole comprises about seven acres and is all freehold. The water power is capable of much greater development than at present.' [11] The waterwheels were probably breastshot; the wheel at Higher Factory had 80 buckets. [12]

George Henry Reed, a millwright and machinist who had trained under John and William Dicker, then used the Higher Factory as a saw mill. His next initiative was to form a company and use the waterwheel to generate electricity and from September 1891 Chagford streets were illuminated at night. Chagford was one of the first places in Devon to have electric lighting. In 1914 the waterwheel was replaced with a turbine. [13] In 1926 this was developing about 21hp on a fall of 11ft 6in and would take the whole river when required. While generating electricity the turbine also powered a Bamford Mill, threshing and crushing machinery. A standby suction gas plant was sometimes used in summer. [14]

From 1930 the enterprise was absorbed into The West Devon Electricity Supply Co. There were upgrades in 1940 and 1948. In 1967 the Chagford unit was connected to the National Grid. Ruins of the old mill buildings remain; a newer structure now houses a modern crossflow turbine installed in 2014. [15]

Downstream, on a private road, Lower Factory – the blanket factory and fulling mill in the nineteenth century – still stands; the leat runs underneath the building, where the waterwheel was once installed. It is now known as Rivervale Close and has been converted into seven apartments or cottages. It is a three-storey building, constructed in granite.
The other two Chagford mills serving the woollen industry in the nineteenth century are detailed overleaf.

Above: the Lower Factory, Chagford, converted to housing. Seven of the eleven bays are just visible here

Left: control gate on the leat, by the weir on the Teign, August 2013

The leat to Higher and Lower Factories in August 2013. Looking towards the hunt kennels by the ruins of the Higher Mill

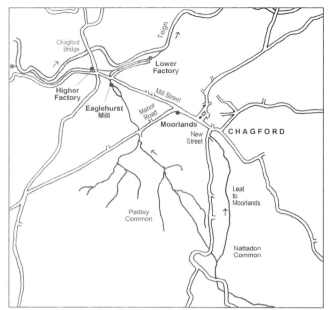

Eaglehurst Mill – later Pond Cottage and now 'Millpond' – and Moorlands in relation to the woollen factories on the leat from the river Teign. Eaglehurst Mill was powered by streams from Nattadon Common where a leat diverged to run to Moorlands

Millpond, Chagford

Previously Eaglehurst Mill, then Pond Cottage
SX 6952 8772. Listed Grade II

It stands near the foot of Mill Street, just below the pond seen on the Ordnance Survey map, fed by the stream that runs down from Padley Common. The building is said to date from the mid-nineteenth century and was converted around the beginning of the twentieth. It is of random granite, with a timber-framed upper floor. An attic was added during the conversion. Fulling was carried on within the ground floor and the first floor was used for drying cloths. A millpond, about 9 ½ feet deep, a dam and a smaller pond stand to the south of the cottage. A separate leat from the millpond is thought to have powered an undershot waterwheel at one end of the building. [1] The town's gas works was situated just downstream.

Moorlands, Mill Street, Chagford

SX 6991 8756. Listed Grade II

Moorlands, built in 1848, was originally a hotel and stands on the site of a 'cloth mill' or woollen mill. The woollen mill appears to have been water-powered, utilising the leat running down from Nattadon Common via New Street and Chagford Fields. It was probably established by Richard Berry of Ashburton at the beginning of the nineteenth century. [1]

It stands by the junction of Mill Street with Manor Road on the left descending to the Teign. [2] Further down Mill Street, off on the right, is Rackfield Cottage. Nearby another house is known as Rack Park. Rackfields were associated with fulling mills. This field may have served Lower Factory, Eaglehurst Mill or the Moorlands site.

Pond Cottage in 1991. Formerly Eaglehurst Mill. *Bridget Cherry/ Courtesy of Devon Heritage Centre*

Moorlands, Mill Street, Chagford. It stands on the site of an early nineteenth-century woollen mill which was powered by a leat running down from New Street, which is still 'live' there. A house across the street is known as Millbrook. Moorlands Hotel was established in 1848. The building now provides residential accommodation

Holy Street Mill, Chagford

SX 6890 8786. Listed Grade II.
English Heritage ID: 1326008

The mill in 1844 by William Spreat, with an overshot waterwheel under the left gable and the river Teign in the foreground. *Royal Albert Memorial Museum*

Holy Street Mill. A recent view with the 12ft Cornish overshot waterwheel – by G. H. Harris of Wadebridge. It was newly installed early in the twentieth century. *Martin Watts*

This was said to be an early mill site, established in the eleventh century. [1] That is disputed: a late medieval origin may be more realistic. [2] Here the Teign makes a loop to the north through woodland. The Holy Street leat cuts across the loop and descends to the mill where it once turned an overshot waterwheel.

But there appear to have been two waterwheels here. A lithograph 'by and after' William Spreat entitled 'Holystreet Mill' and dated 1844 shows a waterwheel on the opposite end of the small building from the one currently installed. [3] When the Holy Street estate was for sale in 1849, Lot 2 was 'Holy Street Mills' which may indicate two waterwheels were then in use – unfortunately the sale notice does not run to details. Edward Aggett was miller and tenant at the time. [4]

This was a favourite subject for nineteenth-century artists, vying for popularity with the now demolished East Ogwell Mill, near Newton

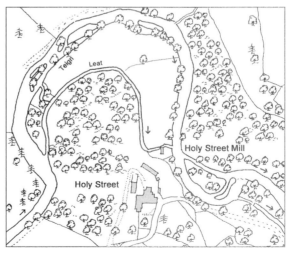

The Teign and the leat to Holy Street Mill. The leat cuts across a loop in the river. From the Ordnance Survey map, 1886

Abbot. Most views show the overshot wheel on the right-hand end of the mill, seen from the Teign. But Charles Frederick Williams made a watercolour of the mill in 1868 showing a narrow overshot wheel on the left-hand gable. As a similar wheel existed under the other gable in 1862, the painting appears to confirm that there were two overshot wheels here in the nineteenth century. [5]

Holy Street Mill in the late nineteenth century, with a narrow waterwheel under the right-hand gable. From a Francis Frith postcard. *Author's collection*

Edward Aggett did not live at Holy Street; the estate was then run as a 50-acre farm by Nicholas Clampitt. He was a local man who farmed at South Hill.

Earlier millers were Edward Coombe, who was milling here in the years 1784-1806, and William Lewis who succeeded him.

Thomas Curzon followed Aggett and was milling in 1857. William Hooper was miller in the decade 1861-1871 but the mill house was uninhabited in 1881. [6]

W. H. Worth recorded a 14ft by 3ft overshot wheel here in March 1934. It was generating electricity at 160 volts and 25 amps output. Apparently the flow of water in the leat in the summer of 1933 was insufficient; the wheel could take a flow of 400 cuft/minute. [7]

The building that exists today is of granite with weather-boarded gables at each end and with a thatched roof; it is considered to date from the eighteenth century. [8] The present waterwheel is a 12ft by 3ft overshot, a typical size for a small mill in the west country. It was cast by G. H. Harris of Wadebridge, Cornwall. [9] It may have arrived just before the First World War when the house was remodelled. Electricity for the house has been generated since the 1920s. [10]

Today the mill has been stripped of machinery and the interior merely houses a modern crossflow turbine, installed in 2011. [11]

Another mill may have existed at one time on the Murchington bank of the river, to the east of Holy Street, but this site has not been confirmed. [12]

The Teign from Chagford to its source at Teign Head

Mills on the two rivers: the North Teign and the South Teign and their main tributary the Blackaton Brook.

The upper Teign catchment is characterised by long leats - the medieval leats to South Zeal and the Southill tinners leat, the Bradford Tinwork leat and the medieval leat to Old Gidleigh Mill which augmented the flow in the Forder Brook.

The Bradford Tinwork leat ran on to the mine in Drewsteignton parish. A forthcoming paper by Michael Moss will delineate its course onwards from its crossing with the Forder Brook

There were other leats here too, providing drinking water to farms, known as potwater leats – not all are shown. An example shown is the leat that ran from the Forder Brook at Aysh to Wonson Manor. This was cut in the early eighteenth century. Below Wyndhurst another leat ran to Coombe, a farm which burnt down 150 years ago.

Leigh Bridge, where the North and South Teign meet. *From an old postcard*

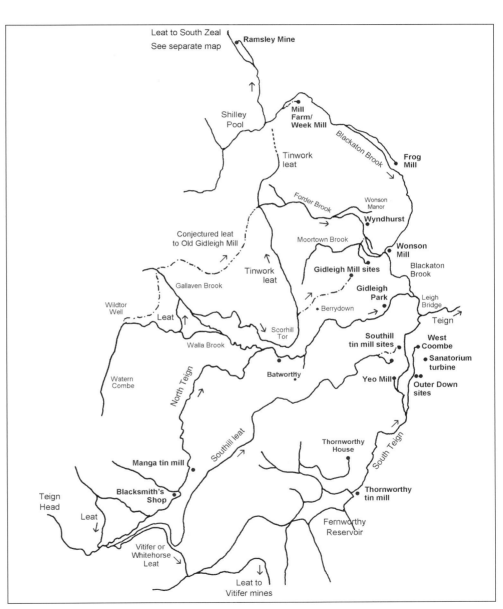

West Coombe, Chagford

Location SX 6831 8713

This site is at the end of a long leat from the South Teign and there was waterpower here in the nineteenth century. The property was for sale in 1873:

'All those Freehold Estates called 'Torr' and 'Coombe' situate about a mile from the town of Chagford containing an unfinished dwelling-house known as Torr House .. ... The farm house and premises on Coombe are within five minutes walk from the dwelling-house; they were erected for the late proprietor some years since, regardless of expense .. having a water wheel, with power for driving a thrashing machine, chaff-cutter, grist mill and apple engine, all of which are fixed .. excellent farm-house .. six labourers cottages .. apply to Richard L. Berry Esq, Chagford ..' [1]
Further notices appeared in 1878 [2] and 1880:
'.. a Model Farm Yard .. thrashing machine, chaff cutter, cider pound and first class corn mill, all driven by water power .. The farm lands comprise about 117a 2r 12p .. Nearly every field is supplied with a constant stream of water brought in stone gutters from the River Teign .. The South Teign River forms the western boundary of the Estate ..' [3]

In 1926 the estate was owned by the Duchy of Cornwall. An overshot waterwheel, of 13ft 4in by 2ft 9in breast was used for farm work and a cider pound. [4]

Outer Down tin blowing mill, Chagford

SX 6821 8658, English Heritage ID: 1406794

Above the leat to West Coombe and shown as 'Blowing House' on the Ordnance Survey map. It was powered by a separate watercourse, now lost. The remains of a rectangular granite structure, built into the hillside, survive in the garden of Outer Down. It consists of two rooms with a wheelpit in the smaller western one, with overall internal dimensions of 11.5m by 5.3m. An unbroken mould-stone and a mortar stone survive in the garden, with a further damaged mould-stone built into the wall of the mill. The waterwheel might have been 10ft diameter by 1ft 4in and would have powered bellows with typical dimensions of 8ft by 2ft 6in. It can be assumed the tin blowing mill functioned before 1700. [1]

Outer Down turbine house, Chagford

SX 6803 8656

Turbine house at Outer Down, seen in 2011. *Tom Greeves*

This was visited by W. H. Worth in December 1926. He recorded a Pelton wheel here, generating about 3hp and driving a dynamo producing 50 volts at 10 amperes to supply lighting to Outer Down house. It was fed by a 10in pipe reducing to 8in, which was about 215 yards long, with a fall of 45ft. The flow at full power was about 49 cuft per minute. [1]

Dartmoor Sanatorium turbine house, Chagford

SX 6849 8691

A small building survives in part of a field known as Smutty Park, the name possibly a – corrupted – reference to a vanished tin blowing mill. Water was piped to the turbine from a tank at SX 6845 8682, fed from a pond. But according to W. H. Worth, water was piped from the West Coombe leat. The turbine was generating electric light for the hospital in 1927. [1]

Yeo Mill, Chagford

SX 6786 8656. Listed Grade II
English Heritage ID: 1326035

Also known as Yeo Farm. The Perryman family lived here from 1545 [1] until at least 1966 [2] – for over four hundred years. The watermill may only date from 1854 when Dicker, the Chagford millwrights, installed a waterwheel. [3] In 1851 John Perryman was merely listed as farmer here. [4]

The present overshot waterwheel, dating from 1877, with wrought iron buckets, has shrouds and segmental ring gear cast by Polyblank & Co, of Newton Abbot. [5] It is 13ft by 3ft 4in breast and used to work at 6 ½ rpm with a flow of 500 cuft per minute. Equipment included two pairs of 4ft millstones, a chaff cutter, a corn crusher and kibbler, a threshing machine and winnower together with a rack saw. [6] It was powered by a leat from the South Teign. William Perryman was miller and farmer in 1891; John Sampson, a journeyman miller, was living in his household and John Webber, his carter, resided at Yeo Cottage. [7]

Two years later the waterwheel was generating electricity:
'.. It was Mr W. J. Perryman's father who

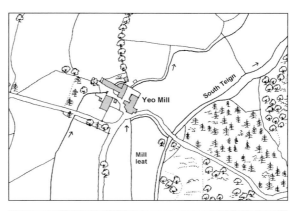

Yeo Mill. From the Ordnance Survey map, 1886

Yeo Mill building at Yeo farm, August 2013. The waterwheel was installed in the extension on the right

introduced electricity to Yeo, and great must have been the excitement on January 4th 1893 when the lights were switched on in the old farmhouse for the first time. The generator was a primitive one .. .. the water wheel and dynamo not only lit the farm at night, but in the daytime worked a flour mill, a bone mill, laundry machines, and even boot cleaning brushes .. Today Yeo is more like a town house than a farm, cooking, ironing, vacuum cleaning and cream-separating all being done by electricity, which is as much home produced as the farm's crops.'

The waterwheel was left in situ. In 1921 it was supplemented by a Gilbert Gilkes & Gordon turbine from Kendal. This worked off a 16ft head. The waterwheel was still generating electricity and powering a rack saw in 1974. [8]

The mill building survives by a bend in the lane, at the farm entrance. Some machinery survives too. William Perryman died in January 1908, aged 66, and is buried in the little graveyard at Providence Bible Christian Chapel, Throwleigh, where he worshipped and preached for many years. He was later accorded this tribute: *'a real son of Devon and a great Christian gentleman'.* [9] William J. Perryman, his son, ran the business during World War Two. Saw milling was still an activity; for example 45 gate 'shettles' were supplied to a customer in November 1940. Various individuals ordered cut logs, one load going to the officers' mess at Teignworthy in January 1941. The turbine was used to thresh and crush oats: 113 bushels of oats were threshed for Mrs Ellis of Waye Barton that month. [10]

Yeo Mill. The pond at the end of the mill leat, August 2013

Southill tin blowing mills, Chagford
SX 6801 8710 and SX 6783 8685

The mills were discovered by Tom Greeves in 1977. Their Southill leat ran from a weir on the North Teign at SX 625 833 to a point near Langridge Gate [OS Long Ridge] and on to Southill. Today its dry course runs on open moorland, partly through Fernworthy Plantation. and also through enclosed land. It was over five miles long and was documented in the 1490s. [1] Fieldwork on the leat was undertaken by Tom Greeves, with Judith Cosford and Jean Rhodes of Chagford in 1990-1991. The leat divided to serve two separate tin mills at Southill. [2] When the 102-acre South Hill estate was auctioned in 1847 reference appears to have been made to these or related sites:
'It is believed the soil is impregnated with Tin or other Ores, there being the remains of ancient Mine Workings on Portions of the Estate ..' [3]

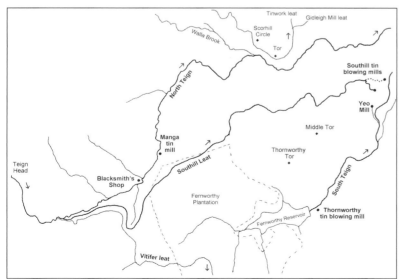

Left: the Southill Leat, its tin blowing mills and its relation to selected nearby water-powered sites on the South Teign and North Teign. It was extant by 1491 and was over five miles long. The mill at SX 6801 8710 measures 10.4 by 4.8m internally. That at SX 6783 8685 is 6.8 by 3.6m internally with a wheelpit 4.0 by 0.65m. In the nineteenth century some of the North Teign water was lost, taken to supplement the Vitifer leat which powered mines near the Warren House. This water then flowed to the Dart. *Adapted from a map by Tom Greeves*

Thornworthy tin blowing mill, Chagford

SX 6723 8443

On the right bank of the South Teign below and to the north east of Fernworthy Reservoir are the remains of a tin blowing mill, which Tom Greeves has recorded as having dimensions of 10.7 by 4.7m; smaller than the Outer Down site which was noted as 11.5 by 5.3m. In the mid-twentieth century the walls still stood nearly a metre high. A mould stone has since been lost. [1]

Small hydro-electric schemes on the South and North Teign rivers

Turbine at Fernworthy reservoir, Chagford
SX 670 843. A 5kW impulse turbine, providing power to the dam-keeper's cottage, was commissioned in 1957.
Thornworthy House, Chagford
SX 670 849. A long leat from a stream on Thornworthy Down once powered a turbine here. The machinery has since been taken out.
Gidleigh Park Hotel, Gidleigh
SX 677 879. On the left bank of the North Teign. There was a turbine here at one time. Most of the infrastructure by the gardens, upstream, remains.
Batworthy, Gidleigh
SX 6554 8710 (intake). A turbine on the right bank of the North Teign provided electricity to Batworthy, near Kestor, via a cable run. [1]

Manga tin mill, Dartmoor Forest

SX 6409 8478

The probable site of a tinner's mill from the seventeenth century or earlier, situated on the right bank of the North Teign. Its internal dimensions are approximately 3.9 by 3.5m.

Thornworthy tin blowing mill. The site seen in April 1992.
Alan Stoyel

Blacksmith's Shop/Fayrecombe tin blowing mill, Dartmoor Forest

SX 6377 8426

Near the ruins of Teignhead Farm, on the left bank of the North Teign, are the ruins of a tinners mill. Tom Greeves has found a document dated 3 May 1457, a record in Latin of a court held at Lydford, which almost certainly refers to this site. It was then described as 'Tynsmyth' at 'Fayrecombe'. He comments:
'.. it is very important as [it is] the earliest known documentary evidence to a tin smelting site located in the field on Dartmoor ..'
A mouldstone remains on site with two ingot moulds cut out of the granite. [1]

The Blacksmith's Shop site with the double mouldstone seen in the foreground, in 1983.
Tom Greeves

Old Gidleigh Mill, Gidleigh

SX 6740 8874, English Heritage ID: 1147641
Gidleigh Mill Farmhouse listed Grade II

In March 1328 Robert de Middlecote, a Clerk in Holy Orders, was indicted for trial for maltreating Agnes, the daughter of Roger, the miller of

Converted barn, with a thatched roof at Gidleigh Mill. Adjoining the byway climbing out of the valley which runs to Gidleigh church

Gidleigh Mill, and for the murder of her unborn child. [1] This site is Old Gidleigh Mill – shown as Gidleigh Mill on Ordnance Survey maps –and was powered by a leat which ran from a spring in Watern Coombe via Wildtor Well, past Headon Hill, to Ruelake Pit and Whitemoor Marsh, dropping down to the Forder Brook. [2] By the seventeenth century this leat was no longer active and has since vanished from the landscape in places. Buildings survive in a steep-sided side valley by a bridleway leading up to Gidleigh church.

At some time after in the sixteenth century a 12-mile-long leat was constructed to Bradford Tinwork in Drewsteignton, costing £1,500. [3] It was led off the Gallaven Brook near Rival Tor and supplemented by a leat from the Walla Brook. It respected the Old Gidleigh Mill leat by taking water from lower down the two streams.

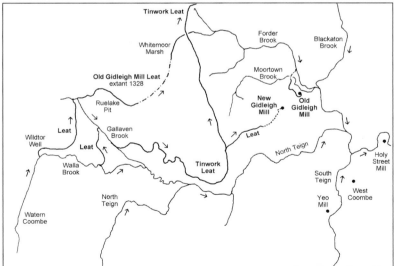

The medieval and seventeenth-century leats to the two Gidleigh mills and a section of the 12-mile-long tinners leat to Blackaton Brook (and on to Bradford Tinwork), constructed in the sixteenth century. Three other sites have been included as reference points. Broken lines indicate conjectured leat courses

New Gidleigh Mill, Gidleigh

SX 6707 8843

In 1655 or 1656 Bartholomew Gidley built the new Gidleigh Mill. He was described as *'a man of great designs and contrivances'* and had recently bought Old Gidleigh Mill together with the Barton of Gidleigh.

The Bradford Tinwork had ceased operations during the Civil War and in 1653 Gidley saw an opportunity to divert water from its abandoned leat to power his new mill. His new leat ran via the grounds of Scorhill then by Gidleigh Castle and on to the watermill. It first ran via Berrydown, as a water-meadow leat, but Gidley became involved in a dispute with Mr Rowe there and was forced to cut a new leat to the mill through Henry Teigncombe's land. In 1687 the owners of Bradford Tinwork reopened their mine and worked on restoring the tinwork leat. It functioned for ten years. Gidley's nephew, another Bartholomew, became the mill's owner in 1696 or thereabouts and had the tinwork leat diverted again in 1697.

A court case, following a petition brought by the adventurers in the tinwork, found in Gidley's favour in 1699 and water continued to flow down the diversionary leat. [1] The mill was still at work in the eighteenth century [2] but no longer exists. The leat that today runs through Gidleigh churchyard is a separate potwater watercourse.

'Blackaton', Throwleigh

SX 6776 8897

A small private hydro-electric plant existed here in 1944, powered by the Blackaton Brook:
'Auction .. Thatched Cottage Residence known as 'Blackaton' well known as the prettiest and best sited property in this charming unspoilt locality .. electricity throughout, central heating, automatic water-wheel gravity water supply .. The grounds and gardens are a feature of the property; Carriage Drive; The Blackawton [sic] Brook winds and flows through the property, affording quite good trout fishing .. Outbuildings, paddocks .. 7 acres.' [1]

Blackaton is close to the site of Wonson Mill. The river runs through its gardens, falling over little rocky weirs; the thatched house was built sometime after 1903 and before 1938. Just upstream, by Blackaton Cross, before the bridge over the river leading to Providence, there is a stone-lined culvert under the lane. This was originally on the leat to Wonson Mill. [2] It was probably re-used to power the waterwheel serving Blackaton.

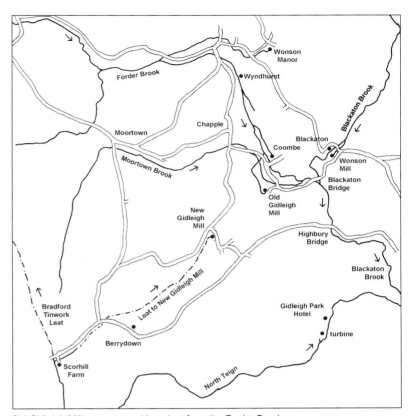

Old Gidleigh Mill was powered by a leat from the Forder Brook, augmented by a leat cut from Watern Coombe on Dartmoor in the medieval period. Buildings remain by the foot of a byway that climbs southwards to Gidleigh church.

Near Gidleigh Church, on the far side of Gidleigh Castle, was the site of New Gidleigh Mill which took its water from the Bradford Tinwork leat. The mill leat is conjectured.

Blackaton appears to have made use of the old leat to Wonson Mill from the Blackaton Brook. Other leats led off the Forder Brook, Coombe farmhouse, burnt down 150 years ago, being served by one. The watercourse serving Wonson Manor was another potwater leat taken off the Forder Brook below Ash. It was dug in 1703. The waterwheel serving Wyndhurst was almost on the river, served by a weir.

Wonson Mill, Throwleigh

SX 6778 8894

This now-vanished mill was the subject of a marriage settlement in 1649, when William Knapman of Throwleigh married Ann Hutton of St Kew, Cornwall. [1] In 1674 Knapman sold the estate for £800:

'.. all that messuage, barton, demesnes, farm and tenement called Wonston, with the mills belonging to it called Wonston Mills ..' [2]

A document from 1675 concerns the intended marriage of William Northmore to Mary, William Knapman's daughter. [3] By 1794 the mill had gone, together with the mill house, and there was no attempt to rebuild either. The estate was then in the hands of the Gidley family, who were still the owners in 1840: *'and one close or acre of land called Mill Hams and Ley Mead and the site or ruins of a house and mill called Wonson Mill ..'* [4]

The mill was powered by the waters of the Blackaton Brook. In the 1930s a millstone was seen in the garden of Blackaton house, opposite the site of the ruins of Wonson Mill. [5]

Wyndhurst, Throwleigh

SX 6726 8946 [waterwheel]

An overshot waterwheel with wooden launder was generating electricity here in 1946, before mains electricity reached the village. It was powered by a short leat from the Forder Brook.

The wheel was built by Percy Wadman. He built a second small waterwheel with buckets to pump water to Wadhurst and to the village hall. It was still working in 2005. This second wheel apparently took water from a well. [1]

Frog Mill, South Tawton

SX 6795 9054

An ancient site, it would appear, just inside the parish boundary with Throwleigh. It was originally been the manorial mill of Aysh. This is not the only mill at the edge of a parish. Week, or Wyke, Mill upstream may have helped to define the edge of Throwleigh parish.

Frog Mill was powered by a mile-long leat from the Blackaton Brook, known in earlier centuries as the Lovebrook, possibly a corruption of the Ludbrook or Loudbrook. It was at work in 1540 when owned by Thomas Carew of Aysh who complained that Blackaton water, which the mill needed to operate, had been diverted into a leat to South Zeal. [1] It featured in a dispute between the Burgoynes and the Knapmans over water rights in 1590. A witness at court, Thomas Dunning, stated that:

'He hath of times heard to contentions between the miller of Wyke Mill which grendeth by the water of the Lovebrook to the said mill, and so from thence to ffrog mill; and that when the miller of Wyke was accused fourteen years ago, he declared that he turned the water on behaulf of ffroggy mill .. and was discharged ..' [2]

It was for sale by auction in 1860, when owned by a member of the Knapman family:

'..Frog Mill, situate in the parish of Southtawton; comprising a good Dwelling-House, Flour and Grist Mills (working two pairs of stones), and necessary outbuildings, and about 9a 2r 10p of .. Land .. The mill is well situated for carrying on a considerable grist and flour trade, near the village of Throwleigh, three miles from Chagford .. To view the premises apply to Mr Browning, the tenant; and for further particulars to Mr J. A. Knapman, of Bowerland, Okehampton, the owner ..' [3]

The miller, John Browning, who probably bought the property and was the son of William Browning, the miller in 1828,[4] had the waterwheel gudgeon repaired at Bodley's Foundry, in Exeter, at some time after 1863. In 1872 he had the mill spindle repaired there and had cog pinions supplied at 2½ in pitch. A wrought iron 2in dia. shaft was made for him in 1879.[5] Frog Mill appears to have been powered by a large-diameter overshot waterwheel.

George Endacott farmed and milled here in 1891 but by 1901 the mill had probably ceased work, as Endacott was merely farming and basket weaving.[6] In 1909 the waterwheel and millstones were for sale:

'Frog Mill, Southtawton. Arthur Coe (instructed by Mr J. S. Browning) will sell by auction at above .. 29 Timber Trees, Water Wheel and Casting, ½ ton of Shafting, three Mill Stones, 60 Sheets of Corrugated Iron, Roofing Tiles, Pig's Troughs, etc.'[7]

Two years later the mill building was auctioned as a source of stone and building materials, together with four acres of land and the mill stream.[8]

A few low stone walls and the dried up millpond, at the end of the leat, remain today by a public footpath.

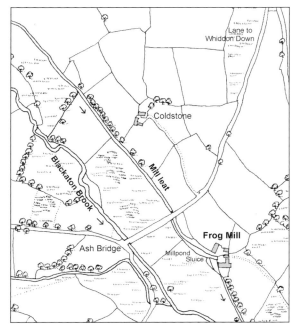

Frog Mill, Throwleigh. From the Ordnance Survey map circa 1890. It was, on present evidence, always a grain mill, powered by water flowing from the Blackaton Brook. The leat was about a mile long

Frog Mill. Dry millpond at the end of the leat from the Blackaton Brook, August 2013

Mill Farm, East Week, Throwleigh
SX 6612 9176

This was the site of the sixteenth-century Wyke Mill. There the miller was able to control the water from the Blackaton Brook to Frog Mill downstream. Water could also be turned away via the Zeal Leat towards South Tawton and the Taw valley. In a court case in 1590 Thomas Dunning provided the evidence:
'He hath often heard to contentions between the miller of Wyke Mill which grendeth by the water descending from the Lovebrook [Blackaton Brook] to the said Mill, and so from thence to ffrog mill; and that when the miller of Wyke Mill was accused fourteen years ago [1576], he declared that he turned the water on behaulf of ffroggy mill but of no contentions between Seale (Zeal) mill and ffrog mill .. and was discharged.' [1]

The site had ceased to be a mill by the early nineteenth century. In 1840 it was known purely as 'Mill' with William Coombe in occupation. [2] In 1841 Coombe was listed as 'Farmer' at Mill Farm. [3] Mill Farm is now a private house, partly rebuilt after a fire in the 1890s. A very large millstone was unearthed here in 1899 or 1900. [4] The last of the Coombes emigrated to Argentina in 1907. [5] The Blackaton Brook falls steeply past the site but the evidence for a leat is now tenuous.

West Gooseford. Dam wall of pond on the right. Across the field can be seen the overgrown stonework of the launder leading to the waterwheel site. March 1997

West Gooseford. Surviving nave for a large waterwheel, probably overshot, March 1997

West Gooseford Farm, South Tawton
SX 6760 9169

This site was powered by a tributary of the Blackaton Brook, a subsidiary of the Teign. A millpond survives, in water, with its stone-built retaining wall at Lower Gooseford. A high stone launder carried an iron pipe to the overshot wheel. This wheel was possibly 24ft in diameter: it had wooden buckets and sole and 10 pairs of arms. Only the shaft and a nave survive together with some shroud fragments in the pit. The waterwheel may have been cast in Newton Abbot in the late-nineteenth century. It provided remote drive via ring gear and transmission rods mounted on stone piers, four of which survive. It generated electricity – one of the earlier hydro-electric plants on the moor. The wheel was said to have been cut up in the 1950s. [1] William Moore farmed West Gooseford until 1853 when he advertised portable threshing and winnowing machines for sale: there was no indication then of water power. [2] The surviving structures are impressive and would have required significant investment, which seems out of all proportion in providing power to a nearby farm.

Bradford Tinwork, Drewsteignton

SX 700 910

Later known as Wheal St Ann

A new paper, intended to be published in 2016, will provide the findings of detailed investigations on the ground into the course of the leat which served the tinwork at Bradford, by Shilstone, Drewsteignton.[1]

This was a significant leat, 12 miles long and it cost £1,500 to construct in the sixteenth century.[2] It took its water from the Gallaven Brook, supplemented by a flow from the Walla Brook, and then ran via Gidleigh and Throwleigh Commons to the Blackaton Brook. For the present, the leat's course via Week or Wyke and Gooseford to Shilstone is purely conjectured. The most impressive construction on this section must have been the wooden launder, allegedly 22 feet high and a quarter of a mile long, at West Week, taking the water across a valley. This was at SX 655 923.[3]

In June 1550 William Knapman junior had presented over 5,000 lbs of tin at the Chagford Coinage. John Knapman acquired the tinwork in 1559.[4] The leat was built by this time and was used until 1653 when mining at Bradford openwork ceased. Bartholomew Gidley utilised the water of the abandoned leat by cutting a diversion to power his new grain mill at Gidleigh.[5]

Right: the 12-mile leat from the Walla Brook to Bradford Tinwork, which was active at least from the sixteenth century until 1653 and again for ten years towards the end of the century. Its course onwards from Throwleigh is conjectured. It respected the course of the medieval leat to Zeal Mill, which had its head weir on the Blackaton Brook, below Shilley Pool. The Tinwork leat took a lower course to West Wyke (or Week) where it crossed the valley on a launder or aqueduct, allegedly 22-feet high and 440-yards long. This is a simplified diagram with other leats and mills in the area omitted for clarity

At Bradford the tinwork was re-opened in 1687 and the leaseholder, Thomas Hodge, a Cornishman, restored the leat spending £4,000.[6] The miners instigated a court case against the owner of Gidleigh Mill but Bartholomew Gidley, nephew of the earlier proprietor, counter-claimed and won his case in 1699; he was able to retain the leat to his mill.[7] The tinwork leat was never used after this time.

Tom Greeves noted that this was one of the richest tinworks of north-east Dartmoor.[8] So it was perhaps unsurprising that later adventurers were tempted to re-open the site. A Bristol company began work in 1846 and sunk a shaft 34 fathoms deep; the adventurers found some copper, tin and silver at this depth in 1848. The mine was then worked by an 18-inch cylinder rotary steam engine but was not a success and

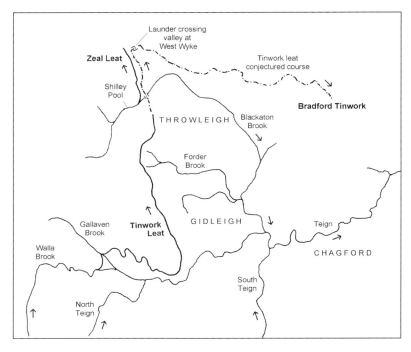

the plant was for sale in March 1849. No water-power was employed and the adits became blocked again [9] and the openwork is now known as Bradford Pool. It is on private land.

Leat to South Zeal

This watercourse was in existence as early as 1243. William Curzon of South Zeal paid the owner of Frog Mill a capital sum to be allowed to take water from the Blackaton Brook. Water was diverted via a head weir below Shilley Pool to sites in the Taw Valley, and in consequence was lost to the Teign. At Drybridge it joins the Ramsley Stream. [1] A tucking mill, later converted to mill grain, at South Zeal was powered by it and in the nineteenth century large water-wheels at Ramsley Mine were worked from a subsidiary leat. Following a court case in 1590 it was determined that Zeal Mill was only to have as much water as could pass through a bull's-eye stone. [2]

Ramsley Copper Mine, South Zeal, South Tawton

Known as Wheal Emily from 1881
SX 6492 9299 [50ft wheel]

The mine was developed significantly in 1858. In February 1860 a 50ft by 4ft waterwheel was installed for pumping and by 1864 a 35ft by 4ft waterwheel was also at work, used for crushing ores. A turbine was used towards the end of the

The Zeal Leat from the Blackaton Brook. Below South Zeal it was known as the Ramsley Stream. This is a schematic rather than a scale map. Some of the information is derived from the 1847 South Tawton tithe map. The leat to Ramsley Mine was constructed after this date. By 1305 South Zeal was a borough, with a planned town straddling the Exeter-Okehampton road. [3] The leat to Tawton Mill from Stenteford Bridge has now gone, although a second arch, now blocked, at the bridge indicates its course

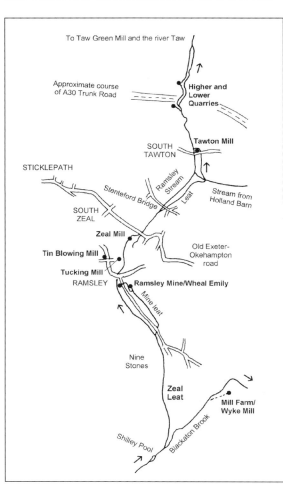

Aqueduct and large overshot waterwheel at Ramsley Mine. From a Chapman and Son photograph. *Courtesy Devon Heritage Services, image reference 1578Z/7296*

century and 966 tons of copper ore were extracted in the years 1883-1887. By 1900 steam power was also used in dry seasons. The workings were abandoned in 1909. [1]

Zeal Mill, South Zeal, South Tawton
SX 6509 9345

Zeal Mill decayed in 1811. The wooden launder has collapsed onto the waterwheel. Etching by Samuel Prout. A grain mill had existed here in 1590. *Devon Heritage Services, image SC2694*

South Zeal used to stand on the main road from Exeter to Okehampton. It was a planned borough within South Tawton parish, in existence by the beginning of the fourteenth century. [1] Zeal was originally a tucking mill, owned by William Curson in the thirteenth century and powered by his leat from the Blackaton Brook; the diversion of water away from Frog Mill led to disputes at various times. It was converted to a grain mill in the mid sixteenth century. [2] In the winter of 1775-76 the overshot wheel was frozen up and William Redmore was killed trying to free it. [3] Samuel Prout portrayed the mill in a decayed state in 1811. [4] It would appear to have been repaired as it was recorded as 'Zeal Mills' in 1841, when Francis Curson, miller, in his sixties, was head of

the household. [5] The mill was a ruin in 1900. [6] A replacement tucking mill was built at Prospect, SX 6488 9313, operational in the decades from 1520, but it burnt down in 1816, when owned by the Curson family. [7] Nearby, at Okehayes, is the site of a tin blowing mill, at SX 6482 9322. Both mills were served by small spring-fed streams or leats, not by the Zeal Leat. [8]

Tawton Mills, South Tawton
SX 6580 9438

In 1718 the Wyndham family, of Orchard Wyndham in Somerset, part owned the manor of Black Hall in South Tawton and the estate included Tawton Mills. They received 4s 6d a year in rent for *'The third part of Two Water Grist Mills called Tawton Mills and half an acre of Meadow [called Mill Ham Meadow] therewith belonging'.* [1]

The mills were offered for sale in 1815:
'.. Lot 2. The Reversion in Fee after three lives, aged 57, 54 and 28, of the Grist Mills, called SOUTH-TAWTON MILLS, now in the occupation of William Fewings, under the conventionary rent of nine shillings yearly, and on the death of each life for a heriot, eighteen shillings. .. for further particulars [apply] to Mr. Croote, Lapford.' [2]

In 1858 they were to let:
'.. TAWTON MILLS, now and for many years past in the occupation of Mr William Fewins, who has carried on an extensive and lucrative business on the premises, together with 4a 1r 8p of meadow and 1a 0r 12p of orchard and garden ground. The mills are .. in the centre of a populous district and the water power never fails ..' [3]
John Partridge was miller in 1871 but quit in 1875. [4] He was succeeded by Richard Williams and then James White was here from 1901. He bought the mill for £1,175 when the Oxenham

estate was for sale in 1911. He was here at least until 1930. Milling ceased in that decade. Carrel Jevons became the owner in 1973 and converted the mill into a residence, restoring one of the two overshot waterwheels as a pitchback. [5]

The waterwheel is 12ft by 4ft and used to drive two pairs of stones. Also on site are a set of gearing including a split-cast iron pit wheel, its teeth missing; a cast-iron wallower; a wooden upright shaft which appears to have been spliced together; a compass-arm spur wheel, all of timber construction, a surviving stone nut of wood with iron bands and wooden cogs and a wooden crown wheel. The second waterwheel was constructed almost entirely from timber and drove a single pair of stones. Three bedstones survived on the stone floor in 2003 – one French burr and two of conglomerate. The fourth stone was missing. [6]

A leat from the Ramsley Stream originally turned the water-wheels. It began by Stenteford Bridge, at SX 6542 9380, and ran southwards to the mill, its flow increased by a stream from Holland Barn.

Tawton Mill, South Tawton, in April 1998

Near the mill, a millpond gave the miller local control over the water. [7] The leat is clearly shown on the 1886 Ordnance Survey 1: 2,500 map but has since vanished from the landscape.

Higher and Lower Quarries, South Tawton
SX 6565 9507

These limestone quarries were developed on a large scale and by 1847 already had two leats fed by the Ramsley Stream. [1] They were to let for a term of five years in 1869 and again in 1874. By 1874 the tenant was J. D. Palmer and the sites included kilns, buildings, watercourses and pumps. [2]

In 1879 the quarries were again to let:
'South Tawton Lime Quarries .. To be Let by Tender, for a term of 5 or 10 years .. all those very desirable Lime Quarries, consisting of three kilns and necessary water-power machinery for carrying on an extensive trade, now in full work, and in the occupation of Mr J. D. Palmer, as tenant .. The Lime from these quarries is of prime quality, and generally averages yearly from 27 to 30,000 bushels ..'
Thomas Lane, of Clare House, Leamington, may have been the owner at the time. [3]

The 1886 Ordnance Survey map clearly shows watercourses, a pond or reservoir, a sluice and an aqueduct amid the workings. An inclined plane in the lower quarry may have been powered by a waterwheel and possibly a crushing plant was also water powered. Today the disused sites are bisected by the A30 Trunk Road. The Ramsley Stream joins the Taw just above Taw Green Mill, augmenting the leat there, its water lost to the Teign.

Mills on the Bovey and the Liverton Brook

The river Bovey at Hisley Bridge near Lustleigh. *David Ayres, Flickr*

Water-powered sites on the Bovey – including grain mills and mines – in Teigngrace, Bovey Tracey, Manaton, North Bovey, Chagford (part), Lustleigh and Moretonhampstead (part) and on the Liverton Brook with sites in Teigngrace and Ilsington

Mills on the Bovey and the Liverton Brook

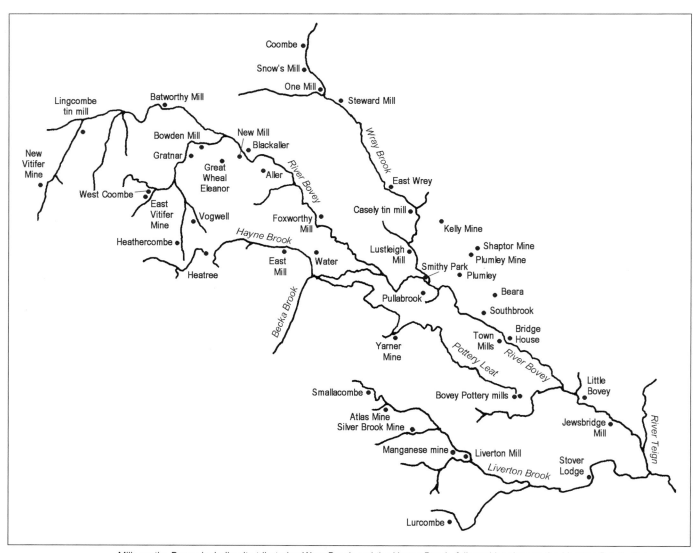

Mills on the Bovey including its tributaries Wray Brook and the Hayne Brook, followed by sites on the Liverton Brook. Sequenced upstream from Jews Bridge Mill near the confluence of the Bovey and the Teign. Water-powered sites include mines, a pottery including a separate flint mill, farm mills, a tannery, a saw mill, a fulling mill and a pump house

Jewsbridge Mill, Teigngrace
SX 8387 7630

This was the lowest mill site on the river Bovey and one of only two known water-powered flint mills in Devon. The second was at Lower Mill/Windsor Mill in the Bovey Pottery complex. A survey of flint mills in Britain undertaken in the 1960s does not list any such site in the county. [1]

The mill was situated just to the south of Jews Bridge; the bridge is now lost under the A38 Devon Expressway. A major weir diverted water into the short mill leat.

In 1890, the Bovey Tracey Pottery Company was importing flints, via Teignmouth, from Dieppe and from Fecamp. [2] Jewsbridge Mill was very likely their destination, reached via the Stover Canal. In that year the mill featured in a legal case relating to poaching in the river. [3]

It was quite a small building but probably incorporated one or two slurry grinding pans, powered by an undershot or low breastshot waterwheel.

Flints were calcined to about 1000°C before being milled in water to a slurry of fine particles; settling and drying processes followed before use in the nearby pottery. Ground flint was used in slipwares; earthenware pots, typically red or buff, would be dipped in liquid clays containing fine white flint powder before being fired in kilns. Josiah Wedgwood was the first to employ this process commercially, to produce his popular creamwares, sometimes with added relief decoration. The calcined flint particles allowed water to escape quickly from the clay coating and made a stronger ceramic product. [4]
Jewsbridge Mill may have been established early in the nineteenth century. Unfortunately it does not feature on the somewhat inadequate Teigngrace tithe map. It was still extant in 1905 but the site had been cleared by 1933. [5]

A pair of water-powered flint mills have been preserved in Staffordshire, at Cheddleton and have been open to the public at weekends between March and October. Mosty Lea Mill at Oulton, near Stone, is another Staffordshire flint mill which has its grinding machinery preserved, together with calcining and drying kilns and a large pitchback waterwheel. This mill is also open to the public on certain days. [6]

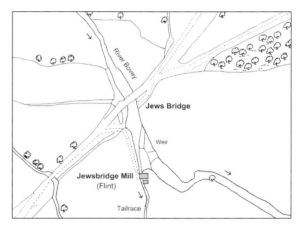

Jewsbridge Mill in 1888. By the old road from Chudleigh to Newton Abbot. The mill's tailrace was used to supplement the water in the Stover Canal. [7] From the Ordnance Survey map

Little Bovey, Bovey Tracey
SX 8318 7679

Tregoning notes that a fulling mill was operating at Little Bovey towards the end of the nineteenth century. The parish had had a fulling mill in the medieval era, functioning in 1327, but not necessarily at this site. [1]
A leat or stream running past Little Bovey is still evident on modern maps, but there is no evidence of a mill here in 1840. [2]

Bovey Pottery, Bovey Tracey

SX 8155 7720

Higher Mill SX 8122 7714

Lower Mill SX 8149 7700

The ball-clay deposits in the Bovey Basin, to the south of Bovey Tracey, were worked in the eighteenth century and such is their quality that they were exported to Staffordshire via the port of Teignmouth. [1] Near Bovey Tracey the clay strata alternate with beds of lignite, a poor coal. Indio pottery, close to the town, was established in the decade 1750-1760 and a second pottery followed nearby, possibly an extension of the Indio site, on land owned by the Earl of Devon. Joseph Wedgwood came from Staffordshire in 1775 and commented:

"I went to Bovey Tracey to see a potwork... It is a poor trifling concern, and conducted in a wretched slovenly manner... We can carry their clay and flints from Devonshire to Staffordshire, there manufacture them into ware, and send it back to their own doors better and cheaper than they can make it!" [2]

By 1794 the lignite pit was 74 feet deep; [3] the coal from the pit being used to fire the pottery kilns. In 1804 the second site had become Honeychurch and Co (Folly Pottery), [4] and was noted as a *'new erected and commodious pottery'.* [5] Buildings were erected, leats were cut and water wheels were installed to power pug mills to mix the clay; others were used to crush flint and haul the clay and lignite from the deepening pit. New bottle kilns were built, some by contractors brought in from Staffordshire, others by local labour. But a shortage of skills and a lack of capital hampered development. [6] The concern failed in 1836 and a detailed advertisement appeared in the local press:

'Mr W. Wills is directed by the Assignees of John and Thomas Honeychurch, Bankrupts. To Sell by Public Auction.. all those .. Leasehold Premises, Folly Pottery, With the Good-will, Stock of Unfinished Ware, Water-wheels, Whims, Mills, Materials and Implements thereon. Situate in the Parish of Bovey Tracey .. held for the residue of a Term of 99 Years .. This Pottery may unhesitatingly be designated one of the largest and most complete in the West of England .. having thereon an inexhaustible Coal Mine, with a Rail Road from the Pit to the Kiln's mouth .. .. Water Wheel 40ft diameter, with Cast Iron Rings, Crushing Flint and Colour Mills, worked by Water Wheels ..' [7]

A plan of the site made in 1837 shows the leats then existing, the Folly Pond – which acted as a reservoir or millpond for the waterwheels – the lignite pit and an engine house. [8]

In 1842 or 1843 John Divett and Captain Buller of Whimple, east Devon, obtained a lease of the old pottery and the coal pit. Folly Pottery became

The pottery leats in 1837. The leat from Becky Falls to the main pond was still to be dug. When Folly Pottery was put on the market in 1836 it already included a 40ft overshot water-wheel used for pumping water from the open-cast coal works. The area underwent significant development in the next fifty years. The Tram Road, opened in 1820, carried granite from the Haytor and Holwell Quarries to the Stover Canal

'Map of Part of Bovey Heath and of several watercourses belonging to The Folly Pottery'. *DHC - D1508M/Maps and Plans/Bovey Tracey/A1*

Some of the 16 bottle kilns at Bovey Pottery, circa 1900. Three muffle kilns survive in 2014. *Both images courtesy Bovey Tracey Heritage Trust*

Higher Mill, Bovey Pottery circa 1900. It was sited south of Pottery Road and the Pottery Pond. Clay was washed and slabbed here before further processing at the pottery. The waterwheel was in the building in the centre, foreground. A tramway, on which some of the workers are standing, led to the pug mill.

the Bovey Tracey Pottery Co. New buildings and machinery were installed and skilled craftsmen were recruited from Staffordshire. By this time the pit was estimated to be about a hundred feet deep: some of the lignite beds were as much as 16 feet thick. The inclined plane hinted at in the 1836 sale notice was probably upgraded:

'[The coal] is brought to the surface by small waggons, which travel up and down a railroad, at an angle, of about thirty or thirty five [degrees], and are put in motion by a whim, which is driven by an overshot waterwheel. There are two of these rails [rail tracks] parallel to each other, so that whilst the full waggon is ascending, the empty one is descending .. On arrival at the surface the waggons are wheeled away to a large shed near the kilns, where the coal is deposited ready for use.' [9]

In all 16 kilns were erected at the pottery.

The leat network was extended; a new leat was cut bringing water from the Becka Brook, a tributary of the River Bovey at Becky Falls, over four miles away. Pottery Pond at the head of the leat powered two waterwheels at the coal pit – one to operate the inclined plane and a second to pump the workings dry. [10]

Flint was used to strengthen the clay and also to make slip for slipware. An improved process for the manufacture of earthenware was patented by Thomas Wentworth Buller in 1849. Local Devon flints were found to be unsuitable and useful

Steam shop in the main pottery complex at SX 814 771: production of flat wares. Steam was used to dry the wares. The building dates from the 1850s. Note the plates stacked on a narrow-gauge tramway truck on the right. *Courtesy Bovey Tracey Heritage Trust*

Pottery being removed from a kiln in saggars. *Bovey Tracey Heritage Trust*

material was shipped in from Beer and from Shoreham. Later shipments came from Fecamp and Dieppe. [11] At one time the company had a flint mill at Jewsbridge, Teigngrace. Bodley's Foundry in Exeter refurbished and replaced worn plant in the pottery in the decade to 1870, including the driving gear to a pug mill. [12]

From 1878 the company was known as John Divett & Co. In 1881 Divett, a magistrate and the acting partner, aged 70, was living at Bridge House, Bovey Tracey, employing 195 staff. [13] He died in 1885. By 1894 the enterprise was failing: trade was poor [14] and work actually ceased for a few months in that year. Charles Davey Blake, of Watts, Blake, Bearne & Co, clay merchants, then took over the concern and planned to extend operations, linking up with some 'northern potters'. Shareholders in the new company were

from Bristol. [15] The opencast coal pit was allowed to flood and is now known as Blue Waters. To the east, German industrialists came to experiment with the local lignite, setting up a laboratory, with generators powered by turbines. The First World War put an end to their activities. [16]

In later operations the pottery still relied on water power from Pottery Pond. Higher Mill, also known as Top Mill, had a 12ft by 4ft overshot waterwheel with cast iron shrouds and arms and wooden buckets. The leat ran on to Lower Mill where flints were fired and burnt and then ground with water in large stone-lined grinding drums. Power here was provided two 6ft diameter Pelton wheels, each with double cups driving line shafting. The ground flint, now liquid, was

The Higher Mill site in Pottery Road, Bovey Tracey, in 2014. Original buildings have survived to serve motor engineers

Right upper: the Bovey Pottery site in the mid-twentieth century, in Pottery Road. Higher Mill and Lower Mill were powered by a leat from Pottery Pond. The pond was supplied by a long leat from the Becka Brook on Dartmoor. A narrow-gauge tramway connected the pottery with the two mills and with a siding from the Great Western's Moretonhampstead branch line. The tramway also ran within some of the pottery shops

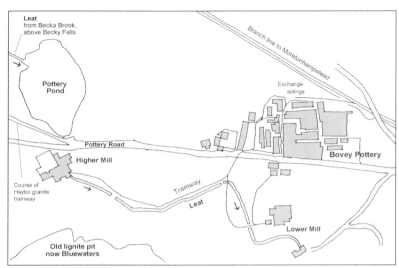

pumped back in a 4in pipe to Higher Mill where it was mixed with clays powered by the overshot wheel. At the pottery a two-cylinder 150hp Davy Paxman steam engine powered some of the machinery including two pug mills. Clay from the Higher Mill ran down to the pottery on trucks running on a narrow-gauge tramway. Warwick Mill, beyond Lower Mill, was also water powered but had ceased work by 1952. [17]

In the mid twentieth century, with kilns no longer reliant on the local lignite, the fuel bill was said to be £6,000 more than if the business had been located in Stoke-on-Trent. Closure came 1956. Buildings were demolished along with most of the kilns. The leat from Becky Falls to Yarner Wood was drained in 1964. [18]   The waterwheel at Higher Mill remains in situ, largely inaccessible, beneath buildings now used as a garage. [19]

Left: The course of the pottery leat in Yarner Wood in July 1999. It served the pottery and, briefly from 1858-1864, the Yarner Copper Mine. In heavy rains, sluices would be opened on the leat at Yarner Wood and at Becky Falls, to avoid flooding at Pottery Pond and Pottery Road. This section of the leat was drained in 1964

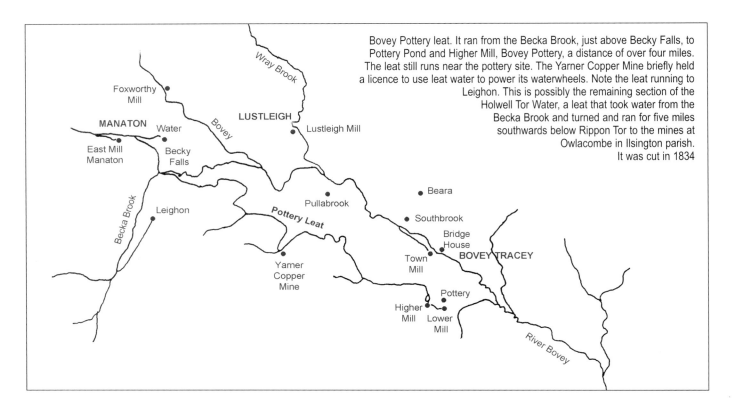

Bovey Pottery leat. It ran from the Becka Brook, just above Becky Falls, to Pottery Pond and Higher Mill, Bovey Pottery, a distance of over four miles. The leat still runs near the pottery site. The Yarner Copper Mine briefly held a licence to use leat water to power its waterwheels. Note the leat running to Leighon. This is possibly the remaining section of the Holwell Tor Water, a leat that took water from the Becka Brook and turned and ran for five miles southwards below Rippon Tor to the mines at Owlacombe in Ilsington parish. It was cut in 1834

Yarner Copper Mine, Bovey Tracey
SX 7837 7837 [engine house]

George Templer, the builder of the Haytor Granite Tramway, owned the Yarner estate in 1828. In that year John Reynolds, from Glamorgan, was granted the right to search for iron ore on the 500-acre property.[1] Templer sold his lands to the Duke of Somerset the following year when his family fortune ran out.

Copper was discovered here in 1858[2] and a mine was developed to exploit it. The shaft was 50 fathoms deep in 1862 and the mine was worked from 1861 by a 60in steam pumping engine, which replaced a 40ft waterwheel. A second waterwheel of 25ft diameter was used for crushing ore and hauling ore from mine, replacing a horse whim. Power for the waterwheels came from the Bovey Pottery leat, completed in 1843. Fifty hands were employed at Yarner mine, but operations ceased in December 1864, the mine having realised 2,300 tons of ore containing about 80 tons of copper.[3] In September 1865 the plant was advertised to be sold.[4]

The site is in Yarner Woods, accessible by the public, but little remains to be seen today. The engine house was a ruin in 1953 and its remains are still visible today.[5]

Bovey Mills, Bovey Tracey

SX 8127 7820

Three grist mills and a malt mill were at work here in 1773, together with a dwelling house, garden and stables. [1] Two waterwheels, possibly more, were installed to drive the four pairs of stones: hence the name Bovey Mills. The waterwheels were powered by water from a long leat; the weir about three-quarters of a mile away to the north west. In 1774 John Soper, a miller of South Brent, leased the establishment from the trustees of the Blue Maids Hospital, Exeter, at a rent of £112 per annum [estimated at £11,930 in 2012], which indicates that this was a significant mill site at that time. [2]

In 1778 the property was advertised to let as:
'.. A compleat Room of GRIST MILLS, lately erected on the best construction .. The new mills consist of two pair of French Stones with every necessary ..
Also a BOLTING MILL, with all conveniences for carrying on the Flour Trade. Two other Mills for grinding malt and barley; a good Dwelling-house, stable, hog-styes, a garden, with two meadows near adjoining the premises, containing eight acres and upwards ..' [3]

Until 1834 the inhabitants of Wreyland, Lustleigh, were obliged to have their grain ground at Bovey Mills. The law was changed in this year and they were able to use Lustleigh Mill. [4]

Mrs Reed was the tenant in 1835 when the leasehold of the mills was offered for sale. William Hole of Parke – now used as the headquarters of the Dartmoor National Park Authority – owned Bovey Mills in 1839. Samuel Ball was the miller then. Dominick Dormer occupied the premises in 1840. A tenant was sought in 1841 and in the following year. [5]

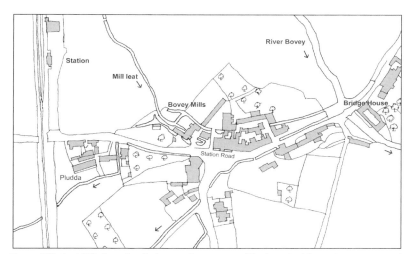

Bovey Mills in 1903, from the Ordnance Survey map. The layout of the watercourses and the plan of the buildings have changed since 1840. About this time – Tregoning states it was in 1910 – a new four and three storey mill complex replaced the earlier buildings, but it was short-lived; the new mill was destroyed in a major conflagration in 1925

Bovey or Town Mills, Bovey Tracey, in 1899, when run by Edward Wyatt. A posed shot with several carters, their horses and wagons.
Courtesy Bovey Tracey Heritage Trust

William Hole's tenant at the mills in 1861 was John Pascoe, a local man, born in the parish in about 1836. The mills worked three pairs of stones together with smut and flour machines. [6]

William Henry Lee, 26, ran the mills with his brother Arthur, 18, and one servant, in 1871. The Lee brothers came from Hennock, where their father farmed Longlands. [7] By this decade Bovey Tracey was thriving. The mills were producing flour as all the millstones were French burr. They

supported at least three bakers in the village; many of the men folk of the parish were employed by Bovey Pottery – as clay washers, throwers, earthenware dippers, earthenware printers, kiln men, waggoners, warehousemen and packers. [8]

Edward Wyatt milled here in 1881; he came from Staverton. [9] Now known as Town Mills, in 1904 a single 14ft by 5ft breastshot waterwheel powered three pairs of stones. The mills belonged to the governors of St John's Hospital and Wyatt remained the tenant. [10]

Edward's son Albert John was miller and forage merchant in 1911, aged 35. [11] About this time the old mill was demolished and a new four-storey building containing roller plant was constructed as its replacement, with a three-storey provender mill adjoining. By 1916 Edward Wyatt owned the property, described as having modern machinery, when it suffered a fire on the top floor. [12]

Albert John Wyatt was proprietor in 1925 when a major fire broke out:
'.. *The provender mills .. were a roaring furnace. There was a waggon load of straw outside, and the fire quickly spread, by means of this, to the stables, where there were five horses. These were with difficulty got out .. The mills contained about 2,000 sacks of flour, wheat, etc, which were destroyed. Two motor cars and a motor cycle in the garage were also burned. The saving of the mills was a hopeless task, and the brigades concentrated their efforts on the offices and the dwelling houses, which were preserved .. The origin of the fire is a mystery. The damage, roughly estimated at £20,000, is understood to be covered by insurance ..*' [13]

Albert Wyatt was a pillar of the local community; he was churchwarden of St John's church, where his only son, Charles Leslie Wyatt was married in 1931, and was a member of the parish council and prominent at the Newton Rotary Club. [14]

Bridge House, Bovey Tracey

SX 8149 7820

Now known as Riverside Mill; the stables are
home to the Devon Guild of Craftsmen. It was
never a mill. The building and waterwheel, which
can be seen from Bovey Bridge, were
constructed in 1850 for John Divett, the owner of
Bovey Tracey Pottery Co. The waterwheel was
used to pump water to a tank at the top of the
tower above, which was then gravity fed to
bathrooms and a kitchen. The system ceased
work in 1920. The waterwheel was restored by
Green and Carter in 1998.

Right: the waterwheel at 'Riverside Mill', seen in February
1996. It was originally breastshot, powered by water in a now-
vanished launder from the Bovey. Water was pumped up to a
reservoir in a tower above the wheel.

Southbrook, Bovey Tracey

SX 8083 7901

In 1839 William Hole of Parke owned
Southbrook [1] and at the end of the nineteenth
century it belonged to William R. Hole, his son.
The 1889 map shows an aqueduct or launder
running to a barn on the estate. In 1895 and again
in 1897 the farm was offered to let:

*'A most productive Dairy Farm of 97 Acres, to be
Let .. known as Southbrook comprising a new and
comfortable farmhouse, convenient outbuildings,
two cottages .. 97 Acres of Land, of which 48
Acres are Pasture and Orchard. The tenant will
have the use of a water wheel, cider pound and
all the barn machinery free of cost ..'* [2]

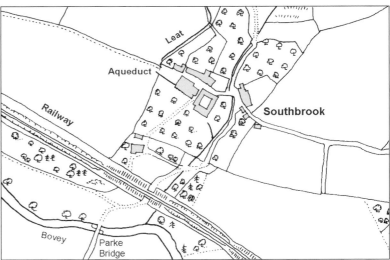

Southbrook, Bovey Tracey. A farm which belonged to the Parke estate. The waterwheel
– its location is indicated by the aqueduct – was powered by a leat fed by springs near
Wolleigh. A second stream running through the property came from Beara. From the
1905 Ordnance Survey map

The property was to let in 1926 and in 1944, when water-power was still available. [3]

A thatched farmhouse survives, which looks older than the late Victorian period; all evidence of the aqueduct has gone, though a stone-lined overflow culvert exists beneath the lawn. The owner in 2005 thought that the waterwheel – very possibly overshot – powered saw machinery and an apple-crushing plant. [4]

Beara, Bovey Tracey

SX 811 794

Water power at this farm site was established by the early nineteenth century, as this notice published in 1815 indicates:

'.. TO be SOLD by private Contract, a Thrashing machine, moved by water, with or without a Wheel of 25 Feet diameter, and all the Apparatus, in perfect repair, on Beera Farm, in the parish of Bovey Tracey. For viewing the same, and for further particulars, apply to Mr. William Honeywill, the tenant; or to Mr John Flood, machine-maker, Chudleigh ...' [1]

This was another property owned by William Hole of Parke in 1839. [2] There is no evidence of a leat or any indication of water power today, although a stream runs through the property. [3]

Pullabrook, Bovey Tracey

SX 7921 7948

Pullabrook was served by a leat a little over a mile long from Trendlebere Down, its water taken from a stream running north-east from Black Hill. The leat ran alongside the modern road from Bovey to Manaton for part of its length. [1] Now listed as Pullabrook Farm, this was known as Pullabrook Mills in 1703. [2]
The leat was still live in 1839 when the property was owned by George Mardon Stook and occupied by William Jackson. It may have subsequently fallen out of use with water diverted to power Yarner Mine on the Bovey Pottery Leat. [3] The farmyard was remodelled by H. T. Eve in the late nineteenth century. [4]

Plumley, Bovey Tracey

SX 8004 8015

A waterwheel pit survives by a range of farm buildings mostly dating from the nineteenth century. The group is listed Grade II by English Heritage and carries the ID 84469. [1]
There were watered meadows on the estate in 1876, but no reference then to water power. [2]

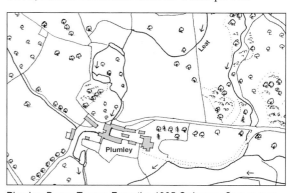

Plumley, Bovey Tracey. From the 1905 Ordnance Survey map

Plumley Mine, Bovey Tracey

SX 804 807

This was a micaceous haematite mine, like the better-known Kelly and Great Rock sites. It had a brief working life: from 1895-1911. In 1907, at the expiration of the lease, the plant was put up for sale. This included a 14ft diameter water-wheel which worked four head of stamps. The site, close to the Bovey Tracey to Moreton-hampstead road, is now much overgrown and there is little evidence remaining here. [1]

Shaptor, Bovey Tracey

SX 806 810

A mine which worked micaceous haematite from 1892 to 1911. Opened by Nelson Bird, it was taken over by G. M. Slatter in 1893. From 1902 Ferrubron Manufacturing Company ran the site. Water power is indicated but not confirmed; a Pelton wheel may have operated here. [1]

Water Mill, Water, Manaton

SX 7590 8081

In 1886 Water was a farm of 307 acres. It was offered to let. The land included arable and rough pasture. Buildings included a house and farm buildings with a water-powered threshing barn. [1] In 1905 much of the estate was woodland and plantations. The waterwheel was still employed by the tenant farmer. [2] It was powered by a leat from the Hayne Brook serving a small millpond. The property came on the market in 1999. The barn, which is thought to date from the early nineteenth century, had been converted to residential use. [3] The waterwheel had gone by this time and had been replaced by one brought in from Palace Mill, Chudleigh. [4]

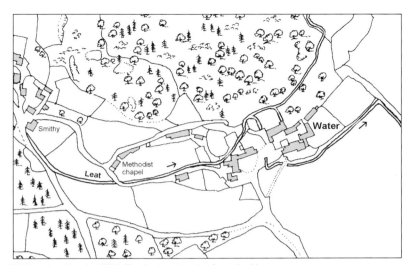

Water, Manaton, in 1905. The leat took water from the Hayne Brook; the tailrace ran on to the river Bovey. From the Ordnance Survey map

The replacement waterwheel at Water in April 1998. It was originally at Palace Mill, Chudleigh. The leat is still in water which is carried to the wheel via a metal trough to the wooden launder seen here. The original waterwheel had ring gear – a detached segment can be seen on its left side. On the wall on the left is an external belt drive wheel, which would have been powered via ring gear on the waterwheel

East Mill, Manaton

SX 7496 8086

Now known as Mill Farm, this was East Mill in the seventeenth century. Peter Tarr owned and occupied the mill in 1800; he was also the owner of West Mill, at Heathercombe, between 1810 and 1830. [1] The mill was powered by a leat from the Hayne Brook which fed a millpond near the waterwheel.

In 1842 the property belonged to Thomas French. John Lewis, originally from Chagford, was miller in the years 1841-1858; by 1861 he had moved to New Mill at North Bovey. [2] In 1858 East Mill was merely described as *'Water Grist Mills'*, when offered to let, equipped with *'two pair of stones'*. [3]

Nathan Stone was the miller in 1861, a native of Drewsteignton. He also farmed, employing William Pulman, 49, as his journeyman miller. [4] Nathan had previously worked as a mason's apprentice and then as a common carrier in Chagford. By 1871 he was farming 150 acres, still milling; he had six sons and the eldest two may have run the mill. Stone was fined in 1874, having been charged with having deficient weights and a balance. [5]

In 1888 the mill formed part of the Wingstone and Hayne estate, with Wingstone House, two cottages and 136 acres, to let as one unit, or with the mill as a separate option. The mill property included a bakery and John Lethbridge Dicker was advertising for *'a good bread baker'* in December that year. [6] Marked as 'East Corn Mill' in 1886, milling had ceased by 1901. [7] In the 1891 census Dicker was listed as 'farmer and baker', born at Chagford circa 1863. In 1901 he was an 'assurance agent' living in Okehampton. [8] J. Harvey farmed sheep at East Mill in 1919. [9]

In the 1970s the granite-and-thatch miller's house, dating from the mid-eighteenth century, was falling into disrepair. The mill had probably been rebuilt early in the nineteenth century. [10] This is a private residence which can be glimpsed from the nearby lane.

East Mill, Manaton. From the Ordnance Survey map, 1886

Foxworthy Mill cottage with the mill beyond, April 1998. The cottage has since been re-roofed in slate

Foxworthy Mill, Lustleigh

SX 7591 8186

It stands beside the boulder-strewn River Bovey at the head of the wooded Lustleigh Cleave. Here the valley steepens noticeably so that the leat to the mill is merely a few yards long. Robert Foxford sold the Foxworthy estate, including the mill, to Edward Furlonge in 1614. [1]

Simon Martin was miller in the mid-nineteenth century; in 1841 and 1851 the site was known as Vernoxworthy Mill. It was to let in 1858 and Martin moved to the Potbridge Inn at Lydford, running it together with a nearby mill. Two of his sons were employed as tin miners. At that time flour and grist milling were carried on. [2] Milling at Foxworthy may have ceased in 1878. By 1885 the mill was falling into disrepair. It was saved by a Mr Hunt who bought the property for £1,750. [3] A secondhand breastshot waterwheel, about 12ft by 4ft, which carries the text *'G. H. Reed, Chagford. Millwright, 1892'*, was installed in 1978 to generate electricity at 7kW. The mill and millhouse originally carried thatched roofs; by 1987 the mill, of random stone construction, was protected by a corrugated concrete asbestos roof. [4] This has since been replaced with slate.

Foxworthy Mill and mill cottage in 1890, somewhat decayed. It had been rescued from complete ruin by Mr Hunt, in 1885. The buildings utilise local Dartmoor materials – granite and thatch.
Totnes Image Bank

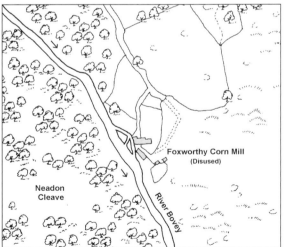

Foxworthy Mill in 1906. It had been disused since the 1880s

Left: the millrace at Foxworthy, seen in April 1998

Aller Mill, North Bovey

SX 7434 8315

There are ponds on the other side of lane from the farm, fed by numerous springs. The property is marked as Aller Mill on Ordnance Survey maps. There is no concrete evidence for a waterwheel here, but it is quite probable that there was one. The estate, then 250 acres, was farmed by William Shears, in 1855. He left in 1865.[1] John Heyward was resident in the decade 1871-1881. In 1871 he farmed 150 acres, employing three men.[2] The Vallance family farmed from at least 1900 to 1931.[3] A converted barn was for sale here in 2014.

Blackaller Mills, North Bovey

SX 7373 8383

On 4 July 1527 Lord Latimer leased a *'tin blowing mill'* at Blackaller to Richard Wanell of Moretonhampstead. It was located on the south side of a fulling mill then in possession of John

Great Wheal Eleanor. The wheelpit structure for the massive 60ft waterwheel. Its shaft bearings would have rested on top of the walls. Seen in October 2012, when visited by the Dartmoor Tinworking Research Group

Alford and John Bremelcombe.[1] Sir John Davey leased Blackaller Mills to Joshua Ales, miller, in 1759. In 1799 he leased the mills to William Dicker, a sergemaker.[2] In 1839 the property was for sale:

'All that tenement called Blackaller and Blackaller Mills, situated in the parish of North Bovey ..and a valuable stream of water taken by a leat from the River Bovey, for many years used by the late Proprietor for working a Woollen Mill ..'[3]

By 1840 ownership of Blackaller *'with site of mills'* passed from William C. Cole to Reverend William Kilmer.[4] So the site appears to have been a grain mill in the eighteenth century, and then converted to a woollen mill, ceasing to operate in 1839. John French, a local man, was farming here in 1871. Did he make use of the leat?[5]

Great Wheal Eleanor, North Bovey

SX 7345 8340

A tin mine on a 300-acre sett on a hillside, then owned by the Earl of Devon, south west of North Bovey village, was re-activated in 1875.

The site had previously been an opencast working; now shafts were sunk, with drainage adits from the new mine. The mine, taken down to 20 fathoms (Hamilton Jenkin states the depth was 30 fathoms), was drained by a 60ft waterwheel erected downslope from the workings, operating flat rods to the pumps in the engine shaft. The huge wheel also appears to have operated a set of stamps and it is possible a smaller wheel or wheels were employed for ore dressing.

Over £500 worth of tin ore was sold before the mine was abandoned in 1881, when the plant was offered for sale. Today the openwork, a millpond and the stone-built wheelpit for the waterwheel survive on private land.[1]

New Corn Mill, North Bovey

SX 7364 8372

Listed Grade II, English Heritage ID: 1306831

New Mill, with two adjoining cottages, appears to date from the mid-nineteenth century, although evidence suggests an earlier building. A mill with two waterwheels probably operated in the late eighteenth century. A double door sited above the nineteenth century waterwheel suggests an earlier layout as do slots cut into the internal face of the granite masonry. These indicate where the timbers of an earlier frame to carry the millstones once rested. The cottages were converted from stabling early in the twentieth century.[1] The mill was powered by a 2,950 yard-long (900m) leat from the River Bovey, with an intake to the north, in woods, at SX 729 842.[2]

In 1841 John Metherill (or Metherell), miller, 25, was resident. He employed William Lanacraft as his live-in assistant. A John Metherell, 55, miller, lived in North Bovey village, possibly his father.[3]

Others milled here in the following decades: William Mortimer was noted as miller in 1850-1;[4] John Lewis, 58, in 1861, employed his nephew Charles Tarr, 27, already a widower, as his journeyman. By 1866 Charles Tarr had taken over the running of the concern, known as Town Mills in a commercial directory of 1870.[5]
Mrs Thomas Ash was here in the 1880s: she was advertising the sale of two 4ft diameter French millstones.[6]

In 1887 the property was offered to let:
'.. *near the village of North Bovey, containing two pairs of Stones, Flour and Smut Machines, constant water supply, a comfortable Dwelling-house, Stable, Piggery, &c with about three acres of Meadow and Arable Land. An oven will be built on the premises if required by a competent*

The stone floor, with two wooden tuns containing the millstones, wooden upright shaft, crown wheel and drives off. April 1987. *Alan Stoyel*

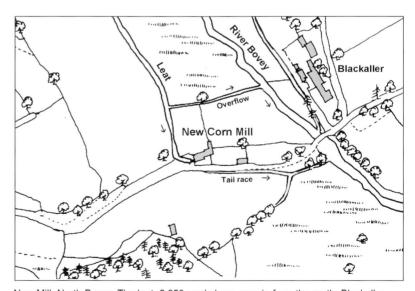

New Mill, North Bovey. The leat, 2,950 yards long, runs in from the north. Blackaller was also the site of a water-powered mill prior to 1840. From the 1886 Ordnance Survey map.

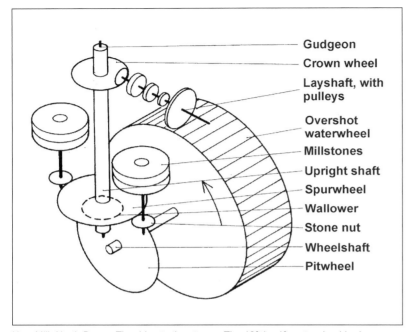

Gudgeon
Crown wheel
Layshaft, with pulleys
Overshot waterwheel
Millstones
Upright shaft
Spurwheel
Wallower
Stone nut
Wheelshaft
Pitwheel

New Mill, North Bovey. The drive to the stones. The 12ft by 4ft waterwheel had a potential power output of 6.85 horsepower, equivalent to roughly 5kW. The 7ft 3in dia. pitwheel was cast in two halves. It has 88 wooden cogs. The wallower is a cast bevel gear with 30 teeth. The wooden spur wheel is over 6ft in diameter and carries 114 cogs at 2¼ in pitch. The stone nuts each have 24 teeth. The crown wheel is a cast iron bevel gear with 84 cogs of 2in pitch. This drove a layshaft via a bevel pinion, working the sack hoist and other ancillary machinery via belt drives. [13]
Drawing and data by Martin Watts

Restored waterwheel by Dicker; probably cast for the Chagford millwrights by Bodley's foundry, Bonhay, Exeter. New buckets were added after 2008. The penstock is by Beare. Seen in 2014

tenant. Application to be made to J. B. Metherell, 12 Albion-hill, Newton Abbot.' [7]

Thomas and John Fice had the running of the mill in the early 1890s but the partnership was dissolved in 1895; John Fice continuing as miller, at least until 1902. [8]

Commercial milling ceased in about 1910. The leat had not been maintained and instead a pond on the hillside provided the waterpower; the mill was workable until 1940. [9] The property had formed part of Lord Hambleden's estate in the twentieth century, until his death in 1928. [10]

The overshot waterwheel, 12ft diameter by 4ft, survives. It is thought to have been cast by W. C. Bodley's foundry at Bonhay, Exeter, for local Chagford millwright Dicker. The iron penstock is by Beare [11] as is the mill machinery, much of which survives inside the building. [12]

The mill is now part of a private residence. It had been used as a store for some years.

The pit gear. Pit wheel, wallower and spur wheel, seen in April 1987. *Alan Stoyel*

Bowden Mill, North Bovey

SX 7243 8403

Listed Grade II. English Heritage ID: 1168289

Grist mills were operating here in 1775. [1] There was a succession of millers from the 1790s onwards: Ananias Pate was here in 1797-1799. [2] By 1806 the mill was being run by his widow, when offered for sale; in 1812 the property was again on the market when occupied by John French and Mrs Pate. [3] Thomas Bovey, born at Moretonhampstead in about 1792, was tenant in the decade 1841-1851. In 1851 Thomas was assisted in the running of the mill by his 17-year-old son John; he also farmed 22 acres, employing one labourer. He was still here in 1856 when the owner sought to sell the mill. [4]

By 1870 William Marks was miller, corn dealer, baker and manure agent and in 1881 he advertised for a '.. *steady Man of good character to Drive a Miller's Waggon.'* [5] He hired a steam traction engine as often as once a fortnight to the benefit of his business. [6] Tragedy struck in 1886. His son Fred was out on Easdon Down, cutting furze for burning. He accidentally cut an artery in his right leg and, failing to apply any form of ligature, died before help arrived. [7] His father was advertising for a milling assistant in 1891 [8] but later that year all his livestock, plant, stock-in-trade and furniture were put up for auction to meet the demands of his creditors. [9]

In January 1892, the mill was for sale: *'Freehold Flour Mills and Bakery, with good Dwelling-House and Land, also Two Life Policies, for Sale. For Investment or Occupation .. auction .. Bowden Mills, North Bovey .. The Mill is in perfect order, there are three pairs of stones, and abundant water power, capable of working 80 to 90 sacks per week. There is also a capital Oven and Bakery, and a large trade in both branches may be done ..'* [10]

The mill, left, and mill cottages, seen from the nearest lane in December 1995. Looking roughly south-south east

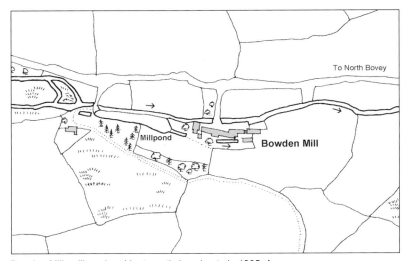

Bowden Mill, millpond and leat, partly in culvert, in 1905. A retaining wall separates the millpond from the river. The present owner has found mortar stones on site, downstream from the mill, indicating that there was a tin stamping mill here, probably active in the sixteenth and/or seventeenth centuries

Marks, having lost his tenancy, then lost his wife: *'I William Marks, late of Bowden Mills, North Bovey hereby give notice that I will not be answerable for any debts contracted by my wife, Jessie Marks, who voluntarily left me five months since ..'* [11]

Mr Hortop was here in 1894. [12] His stay was brief; by 1900 William Cole, was advertising for a miller's carter who could also act as an assistant miller. [13] In 1901 his neighbour at Bowden was William Ford, a baker and confectioner, who employed a journeyman as his assistant. Cole came from Spreyton, born there in 1856. In 1891 he had been miller at Morchard Bishop. His stay at Bowden was also short and in 1911 he had moved to become miller and corn dealer at Steward Mill, Moretonhampstead. [14] Bowden Mill was sold in 1903, possibly to Lord Hambleden, as it was included in the sale of his estate at his death in 1928. [15] The mill has two, formerly three, cottages adjoining. The buildings date from the early nineteenth century. Mr Setter worked it from 1936 to 1948. An overshot waterwheel has been restored by the present owner and the interior is understood to contain the Peak and French millstones and much of the water-powered machinery. [16] Recently a 100 l/s crossflow turbine has been installed, generating 5.5kW. [17]

Gratnar Tin Mill, North Bovey
SX 7201 8362

A tinners mill upstream from Bowden Mill, on the right bank, near a farm, earlier known as Gratnar. It measured about 9.7 by 4.6m internally. The leat began near Barramoor Bridge. The mill was in existence before 1750. [1]

West Coombe, North Bovey
SX 7095 8248

A waterwheel survives out in the open, by the meeting of the Two Moors Way and Mariner's Way. The all-iron (excepting wooden sole and buckets) 9ft by 4ft waterwheel had 30 buckets and six pairs of arms. The ring gear is made up of segments giving a total of 180 teeth. The farm is not now lived in but the land is farmed by the Frasers who live to the east. [1] Richard Perryman, a local from Heatree, once had a tenancy here and had thoughts of restoring the wheel. William Shears of North Bovey, yeoman, owned the property in 1837-1848 and probably for a while after. [2] The farm became the property of the East Vitifer Tin Mining Company in 1874; the mine site upstream from the farm. [3] It was for sale in 1882, with the miners retaining control of the water rights:

'A stream or watercourse flowing through a portion of the estate is subject to lease thereof to the East Vitifer Tin Mining Company for 21 years, from the 24th June 1872, at a yearly rent of £4.' [4]

West Coombe. Shrouds of a waterwheel with ring gear survived by the Two Moors Way in March 1997

East Vitifer Mine, North Bovey
SX 708 823

The mine site is by the Two Moors Way, about an eighth of a mile above West Coombe Farm, towards Coombe Down. A wheelpit and the ruins of dressing floors are visible in a wood. [1] Higher up is the site of a second wheelpit and a reservoir which may have provided the waterpower for the mine wheels. East Vitifer Tin Mining Company worked the sett for at least 15 years until 1882 or so. [2]

Waterpower was developed after 1872 when Susanna Blake Shears, the widow of William Shears, of Aller Farm, North Bovey, residing in Moretonhampstead, granted a lease to the miners:

'Lease of the right to enter a close called Goulds Park to make a watercourse (specifications given) to maintain the watercourse and to use the water for the mining works on the adjoining lands called Coombe Down. Rent – £1 every year for the first three years, and £4 for every year thereafter.' [3]

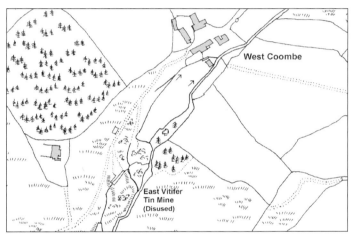

West Coombe and the East Vitifer mine site in 1905. From the 1:2,500 Ordnance Survey map

Below: East Vitifer mine dressing floors in 1970. A waterwheel or waterwheels would have powered stamps and buddles here. *Tom Greeves*

West Mills, Manaton
SX 7187 8102

At Heathercombe. This was Hethacombe West Mills in the early nineteenth century. 'West Mills' was used to distinguish the site from East Mill, now Mill Farm, Manaton. [1] Water power came from a leat fed by the East Webburn River, which turned into the valley at SX 7210 8020. Tom Greeves holds the view that it was probably used by medieval tinners; the leat defines the Manaton parish boundary here, implying it was extant before 1550. [2] At Heathercombe Barn tin streaming was carried out in the fifteenth and sixteenth centuries. [3] A significant leat embankment, six or so feet high, traces of a wheelpit and two millstones remain. [4] It is not known when the grain mill was established. Tom Greeves believes the site had a short life in the early nineteenth century, but it may have existed in the eighteenth century. Benjamin Stanbury was miller here in 1828. Henry Ferris appears to have taken on the running in that year[5] but in 1831 the remainder of the 99-year lease was offered at auction:

'To be Sold .. all that Mill, with the Gear .. which is nearly all new, and also the Dwelling House, Outhouses and Gardens .. Hethacombe West Water Grist Mill .. in the Parish of Manaton .. constant supply of Water, capable of great improvement .. now in the occupation of Mr Henry Ferris, or his Undertenant .. '[6]

By 1842 the mill was in ruins.[7] The leat was later diverted away from the valley to Heatree.[8]

Vogwell Farm, Manaton
SX 7226 8168

A leat from the East Webburn which supplied potwater and powered a waterwheel at Heatree was extended to Vogwell. Here, late in the nineteenth century, it is thought that Robert and John Kitson, owners of the Heatree estate, established a mill[1] with an overshot waterwheel. It was allegedly a saw mill.[2] This was a farm in 1901 and was managed by William Vicary, a 72-year-old widower and his four sons.[3] By 1912 it was advertised to let with a *'.. good farmhouse and buildings, and water-powered machinery. Immediate possession ..'[4]*

The mill barn remains today; the belt drives have been stripped out and the wheelpit filled in.

Heatree, Manaton
SX 7267 8070

Following the demise of water-power at Heathercombe, the leat from the East Webburn was diverted into a new channel which ran round Heatree Down to Heatree. This leat was in existence in 1886, by which time Robert and John Kitson owned the estate, which came to include several nearby farms, including Ford, Vogwell, Easdon and Canna[1] The leat was nearly three-quarters of a mile long and by 1903 powered an overshot waterwheel at a mill at Heatree:

'.. Moorland Farm, called 'Heatree' .. good Farmhouse .. substantial Farm Building .. and about 110 acres of .. Watered Meadow, Pasture and Arable Land, .. and an extensive part of Hameldon .. well supplied with water .. and it has the advantage of a good water-wheel, with .. machinery for threshing and other purposes .. situated on the high road from Ashburton to Chagford ..'[2]

A reservoir on the leat was in existence by 1905.[3] Later the Reverend John Archibald Kitson, cousin of John, had a new leat cut to Heatree. This diverged from the original watercourse at SX 7246 8082.[4] Kitson died in January 1947.[5] His son A. F. Kitson advertised Heatree farm to let in 1944; it then comprised 98 acres of arable and 92 acres of grazing. Electric light was laid on; there was no mention of water power.[6] Heatree House is now an activity centre. The leat from Natsworthy Gate still runs.

Diagram of leats from the East Webburn serving Heathercombe, Heatree and Vogwell. The link from Heatree to Vogwell is not shown on Ordnance Survey maps: water from one of the Heatree ponds was transmitted via clay pipes. The East Webburn is a tributary of the Dart. The Hayne Brook is a tributary of the Bovey

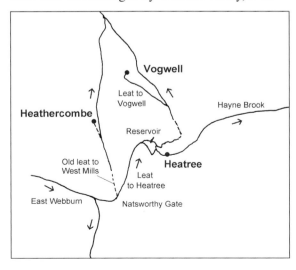

Vogwell

Leat to Vogwell

Hayne Brook

Heathercombe

Reservoir

Old leat to West Mills

Heatree

Leat to Heatree

East Webburn

Natsworthy Gate

Batworthy Mills, Chagford

SX 7134 8520

Listed Grade II, English Heritage ID: 1326016

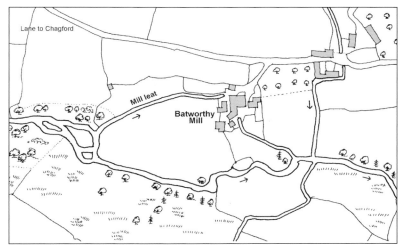

The streams from East Bovey Head and Boveycombe Head combine by Langaford Bridge and form the River Bovey. Batworthy is the first grain mill on the river. The farm and mill are down a granite-walled sunken lane. There is an ancient feel to the place.

It was for sale in 1785:
'A Messuage, Tenement, and Grist Mills, called Batworthy situated in Chagford, in the County of Devon, consisting of a good stone new-built dwelling-house, barn .. and a room of mills .. 30 acres .. now in the possession of William Heard ..' [1]

Batworthy was on the market in 1805 when Robert Tremblett was miller; the owner appears to have been Daniel Coombes, of Ashprington, near Totnes. *'The mills are abundantly supplied at all seasons with water and are well-calculated for a paper-mill or woollen manufactory, in addition to the corn mills now in work.'* [2]

No additional development took place. In 1855 George Endacott, 19 year-old apprentice to Mr Underhill, a master carpenter of Mill Street, was killed in an accident as he was tarring the waterwheel at Batworthy Mills: the tar kettle fell on him and he was so severely burnt, he died from his injuries. [3]

James Collins was miller and farmer in 1851. His son James, 17, was employed in the mill, together with Thomas Ellis, 25. Also living at Higher Batworthy were a waggoner and William Endacott, 13, an errand boy. In 1857 Collins advertised for a journeyman *'to work in a Flour Mill, capable to grind and assist as stoneman'.*

Batworthy Mill and leat in 1905. There was a mill here in the fifteenth century, according to local historian Jane Hayter-Hames

Collins suffered the death of his teenage daughter Mary Ann in 1857. [4] He was advertising the mill to be let in 1866:
'..Flour Mills, containing five pairs of stones, corn and meal elevators, exhaust fans .. two powerful overshot water-wheels .. six-quarter malthouse .. 17 acres .. good labourer's cottage, dwelling house and gardens .. To view and for terms of letting apply on the Premises to Mr James Collins to whom sealed tenders must be delivered ..' [5]

A further notice was published in 1872. The site included:
'.. granary, barn, water-power threshing machine, chaff cutter .. driven by two powerful water wheels .. a very convenient six quarter malt house .. good dwelling-house, walled garden, stables, piggery .. have been in the occupation of the present proprietor and his father, who have carried on a good business nearly 70 years .. Proprietor Mr James Collins ..' [6]

Collins was quite well-to-do: he built Cannon House on the corner of The Square, Chagford, as a lodging house, with 12 principal rooms. [7] He was again seeking a tenant in 1877, by which time he had determined to leave the mill. [8] William Cumming, 33, from North Bovey, was miller in 1881. He employed James Arscott, 16, as his live-in carter. [9] and ran the mill until his death in 1915.

Edward Cumming held the tenancy until 1917 when he appears to have separated from his wife, publicly refusing to pay her debts. [10]

In 1995 the mill had two overshot waterwheels : two were in line and the second wheel, of fibreglass, was abreast the site of a third wheel which had worked barn machinery. The two in line survive. An iron pipe provided water to all three. The mill wheels are possibly 16ft by 3ft; maybe larger. The stone mill building appears to be three stories plus an attic and is thought to date from the eighteenth century. [11] Upstream the leat was live in 1995. Some machinery may remain in the east mill.

The entrance gates are now shut and a 'Private' notice discourages visitors.

Ancient stone buildings at Batworthy, December 1995

Lingcombe tinners mill, Chagford
SX 6883 8440

This site was discovered by Tom Greeves in 2003. 'Smithy Meadow', a field on the north side of the Mariner's Way, was suggestive. Greeves found an extensive spread of tin slag on the surface of the walkers' route, but no evidence – as yet – of a structure, or mouldstone. The slag indicates the probable site of a tin blowing mill, situated by the right bank of the river Bovey. [1]

New Vitifer Mine, Chagford
SX 6787 8276

The mine site is in the North Walla Brook valley – otherwise the Bovey – and evidence remains of the workings including an engine shaft, a stamps platform, a dressing floor and buddles, a whim platform and some surviving masonry from the wheelpit of a large waterwheel. The mine was active in the mid-Victorian period. [1]
Operations ceased in 1875:

The wheelpit at Batworthy, December 1995. On the left can be seen the frame of an overshot wheel: there was a second, in line, nearer the camera. On the right of the water feed pipe was a third waterwheel; this wheel once powered an in-barn threshing machine in an adjacent building

'In Liquidation .. Auction .. at the New Vitifer Mine .. the Whole of the Machinery, Mining Materials, and Effects of the New Vitifer Mining Company, Limited, .. comprising an excellent water wheel, sixty feet diameter, with multiplying gear, iron axle, wood frames, lifters, and ten cast iron stamp heads, with passes complete, one hundred fathoms of launders, sets, stays and hatches, a small water wheel and launders, with gear for working, three circular buddles, cleaning buddles and launders, horse whim, pulleys, kibbles, windlasses, chains, blocks, kieves, rails ..' [2]

Lustleigh Mill in March 1997, seen from the nearby lane. Now a private residence

Smithy Park tinners mill, Lustleigh

SX 7878 8015

Tom Greeves discovered this site in 1999. The Lustleigh tithe apportionment records two fields named Higher Smithy Park and Lower Smithy Park. A significant scatter of tin slag was found at Lower Smithy Park on the left bank of the Bovey above Drakeford Bridge together with the traces of a 540-yard long leat from the river. The slag was analysed and found to contain about 9.5 per cent of tin oxide, as well as iron oxide and titanium. [1]

An undated photograph of the wooden overshot waterwheel at Lustleigh Mill. Note how the launder projects beyond the waterwheel. *Courtesy Lustleigh Community Archive*

Lustleigh Mill, Lustleigh

SX 7855 8095

Lustleigh possessed a watermill in the early seventeenth century, equipped with two pairs of stones. [1] Mill gearing was beginning to develop from a simple transmission at that time: many drives still consisted of a waterwheel, a pair of gears and a pair of stones – the layout used in medieval mills. [2] So Lustleigh Mill, with two pairs of stones, then may have had two waterwheels and these would have been overshot.

The mill was worked by the Cousens (or Cousins) family from the early seventeenth century until the mid-eighteenth century. Members of the family served as church-wardens. [3] By the early eighteenth century the ownership of the mill was split with the Wyndham family of west Somerset owning a third part *'..of Two Water Grist Mills and one acre of land ..'* This statement tends to confirm Lustleigh Mill was equipped with two waterwheels and their gearing. [4] A long leat, from a weir on the Wray Brook, runs through the village to reach the mill, which is situated in a hollow by an old railway viaduct. A wooden launder would have carried the water onto the waterwheels. The mill house is now a residence.

Members of the Hole family were resident for at least eighty years: Thomas Hole was here in 1769. [5] William Hole was miller in 1837 and continued to run the mill until the 1850s. [6] The property was to let in 1875:

The weir at Lustleigh on the Wray Brook. The leat to the mill, running through the village, leads off to the left at the far end of the weir.
Chapman and Son/author's collection

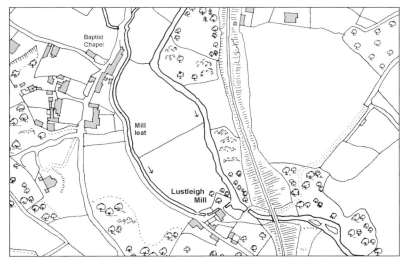

Lustleigh Mill from the Ordnance Survey map of 1906

'..All those Flour and Grist Mills known as 'Lustleigh Mills', together with the dwelling-house, garden and outbuildings; also about 2½ acres of arable and orchard land, with right of common. The mills comprise three pairs of French stones, bunt and smut machines, driven by a water-wheel .. ample space for storing corn .. about a quarter mile from the Lustleigh Station .. For viewing apply to Mr. Hole, Lustleigh ..' [7]

At some time in the nineteenth century the mill's gearing had been updated and there were now three pairs of stones driven by a single water-wheel. William Hole advertised again in the following year and noted:
'The mill is now being put into thorough repair by Messrs Dicker of Chagford, and will be capable of producing 50 to 60 sacks of flour weekly ..' [8]

In the 1870s a bakery was built by the lane, above the mill, to expand trade. George Endicott was miller and baker in 1878. [9] He left in 1888. [10] Samuel Dart took on the business and he and his family delivered bread through snowdrifts in the severe winter of 1891 to reach the residents of North Bovey. [11] Their stay was brief and the mill was offered to let in 1893. It may have been out of use by 1896 and in 1906 it was shown as *'Disused'* on the Ordnance Survey map. [12] The waterwheel and machinery were removed and sold for scrap in the 1960s. [13]

Casely tin blowing mill, Lustleigh
SX 7877 8216

On ground known as Smithy Orchard. It was worked from 1378 or earlier and in 1613 the Lustleigh Glebe Terrier called it *'a Tyn blowing Mill called Caseleigh Smitha'*. Tin slag has been found on the site, on the right bank of the Wray Brook, together with a modern wheelpit. [1]

Kelly Mine, Bovey Tracey

SX 7949 8177

This site is in the care of Kelly Mine Preservation Society. Its members have undertaken quite considerable restoration of the surface works since 1985, a year after the society was formed. A narrow-gauge railway, with a winch-worked inclined plane, links the mine with the processing plant, where a set of Californian stamps has been preserved. An old mine shaft has been refurbished and new headgear erected above it. [1]

Micaceous iron oxide or haematite was mined from 1879 to 1891 and from 1900 until closure in 1946. The Ferrubron company ran the operation from 1917. [2] The ore was used in the production of corrosion-resistant paints.

Two waterwheels are preserved on site. One is a 12ft by 1ft 6in overshot by Willcocks of Buckfastleigh. It was used to power an elevator to carry the ore concentrate in the drying and packing shed to a powered sieve. The second waterwheel is a 16ft diameter overshot, its

Men of the mine's workforce in 1907, when 202 tons of ore were raised. *Lustleigh Community Archive*

The 16ft diameter overshot waterwheel by Willmit of Wellington, restored with new steel arms, naves and buckets.
Kelly Mine Preservation Society

Ore drying shed under restoration, with original 12ft waterwheel by Willcocks of Buckfastleigh. Seen in October 1992. A new launder has since been built and the waterwheel was working in 2014
Alan Stoyel

shrouds cast by William Willmit of Wellington in about 1850. Restoration was completed in 2011; it carries new steel naves, arms and buckets. Originally from Chubworthy Farm, Raddington, Somerset, it now powers a half-scale set of Cornish stamps, generating about one horsepower. Also on site are a turbine – a Gilkes Turgowheel – and an oil engine. These drove an air-compressor for rock drills, the winch and the stamps. [3] Fragments of a waterwheel, made for Dicker, millwrights of Chagford, were found in the main wheelpit in the late 1990s. [4]

The turbine needs a flow of 10 to 15 gallons a minute to power the winch to pull a loaded tram up the inclined plane serving the lower adit. Installed in 1921, it is rated at 3.5 hp at 479 rpm. Water comes from a small pond further up the hillside. A Blackstone oil engine was installed to provide alternative power when the water supply was inadequate. The present unit is a replacement for the original which had been bought second-hand in about 1934.

The society holds an open day for the public bi-annually, generally on the Sunday after the Lustleigh Show. The site is hard by the Bovey Tracey – Moretonhampstead road.

East Wrey, Lustleigh
SX 7806 8284

East Wrey Barton estate was to let in 1915. The 140-acre farm '.. *lies on the main road between Moretonhampstead and Newton Abbot .. the water wheel, threshing machine and other fixed machinery will be included in the letting ..* '.[1]

In 1985 Tom Greeves visited and found the waterwheel still in situ, housed in a barn built of granite, erected in the nineteenth century and standing by the Moretonhampstead - Bovey Tracey road. He recorded it as a 20ft by 3ft wheel, cast for 'Dicker Millwrights Chagford' – the text on the shrouds. The in-barn thresher and gearing had been removed. [2]

The waterwheel was powered by a 430ft-long leat from the Wray Brook, which was still 'live' in the twenty-first century.

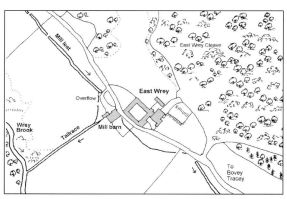

The leat from the Wray Brook to the barn at East Wrey. From the Ordnance Survey map, 1905

Left: the mill barn at East Wrey in September 1996. It may well retain a 20ft waterwheel. The barn stands hard by the Bovey Tracey - Moretonhampstead road

Steward Mill, Moretonhampstead

SX 7649 8527

Steward Mill is shown on Benjamin Donn's *'A Map of the County of Devon'* engraved in 1765. A datestone indicates the present mill building was erected in 1711. In August 1811 the property was known as 'Steward Mills', suggesting that there was more than one waterwheel on site. [1]

Early in the nineteenth century John Nosworthy operated a tannery here. He was bankrupt in 1826 – at a time when many Devon tanneries were short of work following the peace after the Napoleonic wars – and the sale notice gives a good description of the concern:

'All that TAN-YARD, 61 feet 6 inches, by 45 feet, inclosed by a Wall; containing 59 Tan-Pits, with a Copper Furnace, spacious Courtlage, and valuable Stream of Water, with which a Bark-Mill is worked; a commodious Drying Shed over the said Tan Yard, 60 feet 6 inches by 22 feet 6 inches; two Store-Rooms, one 28 feet by 14, and the other 18 feet by 14, Bark-house, Work-house, &c –The Buildings are all in excellent repair and situate and being at Steward, within a mile of the market-town of Moretonhampstead .. a neighbourhood where plenty of Bark may be obtained at a small expense of carriage ..' [2]

Devon was one of the leading counties in the country producing leather: it possessed plenty of oak, its bark used to make tannic acid; water-power to work the grinding machinery and tan-pit pumps, and Red Ruby cattle. This breed of cattle produced excellent hides. Two other tanneries operated in the parish – one at Lime Street, in the Town and another at Leign, Doccombe. These may have used horse-power to grind the oak bark. [3]

By 1836 Steward Mill was functioning both as a tannery and as a grist mill. The tan pits had increased to 66 and the grist mill had two pairs of stones installed. The two functions imply the site was equipped with at least two waterwheels. [4]

Tanning had ceased before 1849, when the *'..Flour and Grist Mills .. with the Dwelling-House attached ..'* were offered to let, having recently been refitted. Dominic Dormer was miller at the time. [5] William Metherell, 22, was miller in 1851; he hailed from Combeinteignhead. [6] William Snow owned Steward Mill in 1860; in that year it was being worked by

Steward Mill before the installation of the waterwheel by Bartle, a Cornish founder based at Carn Brea.
E. M. Gardner/Alan Stoyel collection

The imported waterwheel cast by Bartle, seen in January 1987.
Alan Stoyel

Millpond above Steward Mill, seen in April 1995

One Mill, Moretonhampstead
SX 7592 8559

This was a woollen mill early in the nineteenth century: Mr White of Ashburton purchased One Mill in 1799 and by 27 June had a carding and scribbling machine installed and at work. The mill was situated 'at the bottom of Long-meadow'. White employed child labour here and in 1802 the 12-year-old daughter of Richard Hutchings had her left arm broken when her apron caught in the axle of the great cylinder. In 1806 a fire destroyed practically the whole building and some of the machinery. [1]

In 1839-1841 the property was occupied by Samuel Waldron, an agricultural labourer. It was owned by the Earl of Devon. [2] The building then appears to have been refitted – perhaps rebuilt – and worked as a flour mill, as two pairs of millstones and associated machinery were for sale in 1867, together with the waterwheel:
'One Mill, Moretonhampstead. Near the Railway station. Mr W. Fewins will Sell by Auction at the above Mill, on Tuesday the 3rd day of December next .. one Pair of good French MILL STONES, four feet in diameter, one Pair of Welsh and Moor ditto, with the necessary machinery for dressing the same, Water Wheel 11ft by 3ft 3in; also Household Furniture, Gig, Harness &c.' [3]

The mill appears to have been powered by the Wray Brook. The Moretonhampstead branch railway had opened the previous year and large steam-powered mills at Newton Abbot probably made mills at Moreton uncompetitive. [4]

Mr Arscott. [7] A year later James Pack, 34, a native of Stoodleigh, near Tiverton, was master miller. He was still resident in 1871. [8] Others who milled at Steward were John Fuke, in 1878 and Thomas Taylor, here in 1908. [9] The mill was sold by Robert Crump to William Frederick Danvers Smith of Moreton, the grandson of the founder of W. H. Smith, for £800 in 1911. He became Viscount Hambleden in 1913 and died in 1928 when the mill was again on the market. [10]

Steward Mill was served by a large millpond, supplied by the Wray Brook and its tributaries the Wadley Brook and a stream from South Kingwell. The mill is now a residence which retains a turning waterwheel – a late twentieth-century import. It carries the ironfounder's name on the shroud: 'F. Bartle & Sons Carn Brea 1888': a Cornish wheel. [11] It is an overshot, with iron arms and shrouds, about 12ft diameter by 3ft breast.

Millbrook or Snow's Mill, Moretonhampstead

SX 7550 8628

There was a grist mill at the foot of Lime Street towards the end of the eighteenth century. [1] But George Friend states that the site was occupied by a fulling mill, and may have operated as such since medieval times. It then became a pasteboard mill, employing ten water-powered hammers. The board was used to pack bales of serges: but the mill closed in 1826. [2] Confirmation of the existence of an old paper mill comes from the Moretonhampstead census of 1851.

John Snow was running the mill in 1864. Together with Samuel Vicary he was taken into custody for cutting down a large elm tree in the dead of night on a neighbour's field. The tree was valued at £32, which formed the major part of the fine imposed on Snow and Vicary. [3]

Elm trees were useful as their wood was ideal for the buckets and paddles of waterwheels, provided it was kept constantly wet or very dry. It was thus suitable for buckets on wheels that were undercover or worked regularly. However, if wetted and dried continuously, elm will rot quickly. [4]

By Snow's time, the mill had reverted to grinding grain. He was listed as a miller at Millbrook, aged 45, in 1871. He was also blind and single. It must have been quite a challenge to operate a working mill with all its machinery but lacking sight. It is possible that Vicary or others assisted him. By 1881 he was still living at Millbrook and had retired. It may well be that the mill had ceased work by this time. [5]

Coombe Farm, Moretonhampstead

SX 7547 8702

Coombe in March 2005, when the property was for sale. The waterwheel is housed in the lean-to on the right, attached to the large barn

This farm had water-power from at least the mid-nineteenth century. The barn, with granary, dates from that time. It is Listed Grade II. [1]
A sale notice in 1872 provides detail:
'At Coombe Farm-House, Moretonhampstead, 102 Acres of Corn in Ground .. now growing upon Coombe Hill and Willingstone Farms, the property of Mr William Hayward, quitting the Farms .. There is a barn and Water Power Threshing Machine available for the purchaser .. to view apply at Hill Farm House ..' [2]

An overshot waterwheel survives; it was installed after Mr Hayward's time and carries this text on the shrouds:
'H. BEARE & SONS 1893 NEWTON ABBOT'. Beare was a noted south Devon ironfounder and several of his waterwheels have survived into the twenty-first century. [3] In the early twentieth century the farm formed part of Lord Hambleden's North Bovey estate which came onto the market in November 1928, following his death. [4] In addition to the barn and its waterwheel, the leat from the Wray Brook and a millpond are also extant.

The Liverton Brook

Stover Lodge Farm, Teigngrace
Location not known

James Templer of Stover House insured a water-powered grain mill and stable on his estate in 1803 for £100; the waterwheel and gearing were insured for a further £150. [1] The Templer family sold the estate to the Duke of Somerset in 1827-1828. This is an extract from the detailed sale notice:

'.. MANSION CALLED STOVER LODGE .. STOVER LODGE FARM, with numerous woods, and thriving plantations, with a corn mill, and thrashing machine, worked by a never failing stream of water; barn, stables, &c ..' [2]

The very limited tithe map for Teigngrace, delineated in 1838, is no help in identifying the site. The present-day Twelve Oaks Farm is a possible candidate.

Lurcombe, Bickington
SX 7986 7337

A farm hidden away in a valley to the north of the A38 Trunk Road.

The 1905 Ordnance Survey map shows a pond and a leat leading to the farm, both of which were absent on the first edition 25inch map published in the 1880s. So the farm had water power in 1905, evident by this announcement made in July 1909:

'Bickington, South Devon. To be Let, by Tender .. Farm known as 'Lurcombe' .. close to the village of Bickington, at present in the occupation of Mr W. H. Harvey .. about 175 3/4 acres .. with farmhouse and good set of modern farm buildings, and water wheel ..' [1]

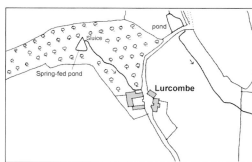

Lurcombe Farm, with pond and leat. From the 1905 Ordnance Survey map

Left: Lurcombe seen from the old A38 trunk road, overlooking the newer A38 Devon Expressway

Liverton Mills, Ilsington

SX 8025 7518. Also known as Levaton Mills

William Soper had been the miller here in 1770. Following his death the mills were offered on lease: *'All those well-accustomed Water Griest Mills called Levaton Mills, with two Meadows and an Orchard adjoining, containing about three acres, .. in the parish of Ilsington ..'* [1]
The property was insured by George Wills in October 1803; his tenant was miller William Osmond. The mill house and grain mill were of stone and cob, roofed in thatch and insured for £180: 'On the water wheels, standing and going *gears, machines, millstones .. therein £20. Warranted no steam engine'.* [2]
In December 1804 the waterwheels and mill gear were insured for £100, which suggests a millwright had carried out work to the waterwheels and possibly the machinery too. [3] Many waterwheels at that time were constructed of wood and decayed over time and had to be replaced. Charles Corbyn Wills owned the site in 1838; his tenant was John Thorn. The estate was then a little over two acres. [4]

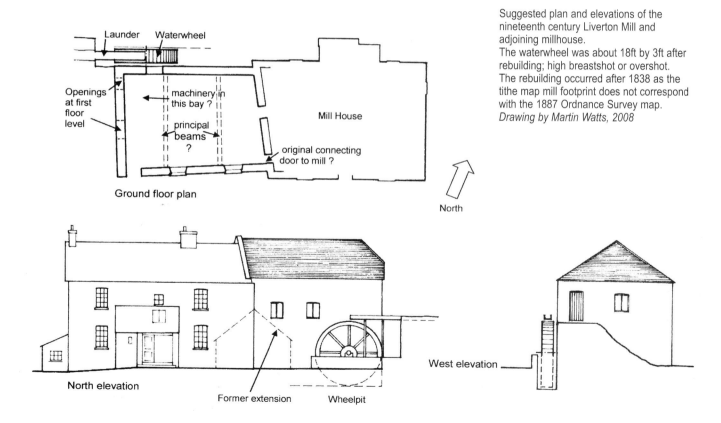

Suggested plan and elevations of the nineteenth century Liverton Mill and adjoining millhouse.
The waterwheel was about 18ft by 3ft after rebuilding; high breastshot or overshot.
The rebuilding occurred after 1838 as the tithe map mill footprint does not correspond with the 1887 Ordnance Survey map.
Drawing by Martin Watts, 2008

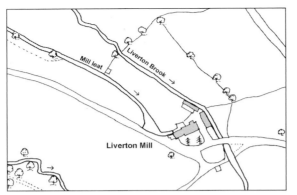

Liverton Mill. From the 1887 Ordnance Survey map

George Mortimore was miller from at least 1850 to 1857 or later. In 1857 the property was auctioned and the mill gear was '.. driving at present two pair of stones, which power might be doubled at a small expense'. [5] Others followed: George Matthews milled here in 1866 and George Andrews from about 1867 to 1886. [6] He was born in South Brent in about 1823, and in 1871 was also farming 10 acres at Liverton. [7]

In 1886 the mill was destroyed by fire:
'Liverton Flour Mills, situate near Bovey Tracey, and in occupation of Mr. George Andrews, were completely destroyed by fire on Sunday morning, as well as part of the dwelling-house adjoining the mills. The inmates at the time consisted of three persons – Mr and Mrs Andrews .. and a lad about 12 .. Charles Batten. The latter was the first to raise the alarm, just in time for his master and mistress to get down the stairs .. The mills consisted of three sets of stones. A lot of wheat and maize, together with bags, have been destroyed, and there were also two carts and a waggon burnt in a linhay .. It is thought the fire originated here .. Mr Andrews has occupied the mill about 20 years. He affected an insurance last Midsummer in the Commercial Union Office .. for £1,100, which it is considered will fully cover the loss. Mr Joseph Coome, of Marsh Mills, Newton St Cyres, is the owner of the property ..' [8]

The mill was not rebuilt when the property was auctioned in 1890:
'Auction .. Lot 3. .. 'Liverton Mill House', Ilsington, comprising a nice modern cottage with good accommodation, excellent outhouses, garden .. with trout stream and site of old mill .. in all about 6 acres .. let to Mr Rowe at the moderate rent of £40 a year.' [9]

It is clear that the mill was upgraded during the nineteenth century. The old waterwheels were dispensed with and replaced by a single waterwheel. The mill gearing was modernised and the new waterwheel drove three pairs of stones instead of two. By 1883 a steam engine had been installed. It was second-hand and had been acquired from the nearby Silver Brook Mine. [10]

Today the residence incorporates part of the ruined watermill. The mill building has recently been rebuilt with three floors and a lucam. [11]

A 'Knokkinge Myll lying in Levaton' was recorded in 1566, when held by George Ford. This was a tin stamping mill. Its exact location is unknown. [12]

Manganese mine, Pool estate, Ilsington
Location not certain

Thomas Widger owned the Pool Willis and Liverton Estate in 1814. In that year he granted John Hatherly the lease of a manganese mine for a term of 14 years. New drifts, shafts, pits, leats and watercourses were permitted and Hatherly was able to *'erect any house or houses, shed or sheds, engine or engines, or other machines or buildings which [he] think necessary for the better working of the said ground .. John Hatherly .. to alter, build and repair the old mill house on Pool Estate and the same to convert into a mill for grinding manganese with liberty to use the same together with the courtlage and streams of water in Pool Meadow.'*

A similar lease was drawn up at the same time between Richard Knowling, tenant, Charles Corbyn Wills, owner, and John Hatherly, adventurer, concerning authority to *'land, wash, clean and prepare manganese'* or any other mineral on Cot Meadow, Ilsington. [1] Manganese Field, item 876 on the tithe map, lies to the west of Pool farmhouse, at SX 7969 7539, and was owned by Thomas Widger in 1838. Pool Meadow, as such, did not exist in 1838. [2] Conceivably the old mill referred to is the one at Liverton, although there is evidence that this was refurbished in 1804. It appears more probable that another mill existed before 1838, above it, on the Liverton Brook. The site was on the Pool estate.

Silver Brook Mine, Ilsington
SX 78934 75835, Dressing floors SX 7893 7581
English Heritage ID: 1433449

Phil Newman reported on this mine site for English Heritage in 2005. He found that it may have existed in the seventeenth century, possibly as a tin mine. More exploration followed in the eighteenth century. In the mid-nineteenth century there were two steam engines here – one for pumping and one for winding. In June 1852 a local paper reported: *'A powerful steam engine is being erected at Silver Brook Mine. The lode is considered good, and probably extends as far as the Hennock Silver Lead Mines'.* Lead and zinc were the ores raised, together with a little silver. [1] In April 1853 came the news that: *'A valuable lode of lead has been discovered at Silver Brook Mine, near Ilsington ...'* [2]

In the autumn of 1856 it was reported that 232 tons of zinc ore had been sold for £663. A large quantity of zinc and lead was still being produced in the spring of 1857. [3] But the enterprise folded that year and the plant was sold off, including a 20in pumping engine, a 10in whim engine, a horse whim, launders and a 7ft waterwheel which had powered a buddle or buddles. The two derelict engine houses remain. [4]

Atlas and Smallacombe Mines, Ilsington
SX 7813 7658

There was a tin mine at Smallacombe in the early sixteenth century when the Marquis of Exeter was one of the shareholders.

In the nineteenth century there was also an openwork, worked as an iron mine, active from 1858. Tin ore was raised from the mine, from three lodes. There were two shafts, one 20 fathoms deep, worked by a steam engine, and a second of 35, worked by a horse whim. The workforce included 25 miners and another 12 or so at surface. [1]

One of the key surviving features of the sett is a largely intact burning house (Listed Grade II, at SX 7810 7653), said to be *'the best example of a reverberatory calciner in the country'.* Its function was to separate arsenic from the tin ore, which could then be used as a metal alloy, for clarifying glass and as a paint pigment. [2] It is built largely of dressed granite blocks.
A tramway conveyed the ore eastwards from

Atlas Mine. The 30ft diameter water-wheel, launder and 24 head of stamps, circa 1900. The wheel was sited close to the burning house, which has survived on private land, at Middlecott. The wheel was powered by water from Middlecott pond.
Tom Greeves collection

raised in a year, and that was in 1890, when 27 miners were employed underground and a further 18 staff worked at the surface. [9]

In the later period of working, certainly from the 1890s, the mine was managed by William Ambrose Grose. His sons Ambrose and Pharaoh were both miners here. Over six tons of black tin were produced between 1901 and 1903, but by 1904 mining had virtually stopped. In this working of the sett a 30ft waterwheel powered the stamps. It was located to the south of the burning house – its wheelpit survives – and was powered by water brought from Middlecott Pond on wooden launders running around the burning house. The stamps could also be driven by a steam engine. [10]

A sale of mine plant was advertised in 1910:
'.. Atlas Mine, Ilsington .. Auction .. the whole of the Machinery and Plant .. including Double Cylinder Portable Engine by H. Sykes, London; Stamps Axle with 7ft Crown Driving Wheel to drive 16 heads Cornish Stamps; 30ft Water-wheel, Stamps Axle to drive heads Cornish Stamps; Water-wheel, 6ft diameter; 16 Heads Stamps, with Stands and Plummer Blocks (have done little work); powerful Crabb Winch, 45 Cwt Steel Tram Rails, 2 Tram Waggons .. 2 Engine Houses as erected, covered with Galvanised Iron ..' [11]
In 1913, under the title Albion Mine, a further working apparently took place before complete closure. [12]

mine adits to Middlecott Wood, the site of the burning house and – in the 1860s – a large diameter waterwheel. This was used to power ore stamps. Forty staff were employed at the mine in 1862 [3] but in 1863 liquidators were appointed to wind up the Atlas Mining and Smelting Company (Limited). [4] It appears that iron mining continued, for in 1864 1,300 tons of brown haematite were recovered. 1,300 tons of iron ore had been shipped from Kingswear in the previous year. Totnes was nearer the mine, but its dues were prohibitively expensive. [5]

The sett was leased again in 1871. [6] In 1872 Alfred Lyon of Middlecott House, Ilsington granted a 42-year lease to Faithful Cookson of New Bond Street, London, which gave him authority to divert water, construct new leats, reservoirs and watercourses as part of a mining development for iron ore. [7]
In 1873 the Atlas and Smallacombe Mines merged under the management of the Native Iron Ore Company Ltd. [8] It was hoped that 10 tons of tin ore would be raised per month but this prospect was never realised: 19 tons of ore was the most tin

Smallacombe, Ilsington
SX 7764 7690

At Smallacombe farm a leat is shown on the 1: 2,500 Ordnance Survey map for 1886, running on an aqueduct or launder to a probable water-wheel site adjoining a building, possibly a barn.

Other water-powered sites in the Teign catchment

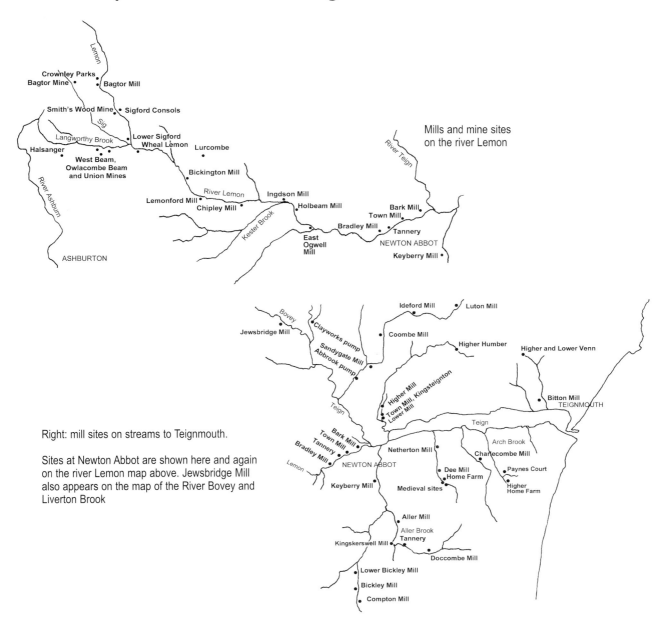

Mills and mine sites on the river Lemon

Right: mill sites on streams to Teignmouth.

Sites at Newton Abbot are shown here and again on the river Lemon map above. Jewsbridge Mill also appears on the map of the River Bovey and Liverton Brook

Other water-powered sites in the Teign catchment

Sites on the river Lemon and the Langworthy Brook

Bark Mill, Newton Abbot
Mill for grinding oak bark for use in tanneries
SX 8632 7166

Town Mill, Newton Abbot
Also known as Town Mills, Newton Mills
Grain mill
SX 8589 7139

Tanneries, Newton Abbot
SX 8566 7129 – two sites

Bradley Mill, Newton Abbot
*Paper mill 1790-1793; yarn mill 1803;
paper mills 1842-1844; fellmongery 1890*
SX 8534 7107

East Ogwell Mill, Ogwell
Grain mill, demolished; features in paintings
SX 8408 7090

Holbeam Mill, Ogwell
Edge-tool mill until 1943
SX 8316 7109

Ingsdon Mill, Ilsington
Grain mill
SX 8227 7197

Chipley Mill, Bickington
*Grain mill, then a bone mill, disused by 1886.
Live leat. A waterwheel in situ in 1998*
SX 8106 7184

Lemonford Mill, Bickington
Grain mill, destroyed by fire in 1884
SX 7985 7201

Bickington Mill, Bickington
*Grain mill 1771; woollen mill by 1850; flock mill
circa 1899-1921*
SX 7945 7266

Wheal Lemon, Ilsington
Mine
SX 787 734

Owlacombe Beam and Union Mines, Ashburton
*Mines, with several large waterwheels, supplied
by several leats*
SX 771 733 (Owlacombe), SX 768 733 (Union)

West Beam, Ashburton
Mine (wheelpit)
SX 7681 7334

Halsanger, Ashburton
SX 7574 7334
*Farm mill. Leat from Langworthy Brook,
augmented by leat from River Ashburn.
Waterwheel, 20ft overshot minus buckets, in situ*

Lower Sigford, Ilsington
Mill site
SX 7781 7385

Sigford Consols, Ilsington
Mine
SX 773 750

Smith's Wood, Ilsington
Mine
SX 773 748

Bagtor House, Ilsington
SX 7665 7520 (house)
*Recent micro-hydro plant with Pelton wheel;
rebuild of an old system*

Bagtor Mill, Ilsington
Grain mill. Retains overshot waterwheel by Beare
SX 7687 7550

Crownley Parks, Ilsington
Dressing floors for Bagtor Mine
SX 7667 7585

Bagtor Mine, Ilsington
Wheelpit(s)
SX 761 755

Bradley Mill leat in Bradley Woods. From an old postcard. *Author's collection*

Chipley Mill, Bickington, hard by the Ashburton-Newton Abbot road. Seen in September 1960. The leat was still live in the 1990s and an overshot waterwheel with wooden buckets was in place. *Alan Stoyel*

East Ogwell Mill, Ogwell, since demolished, with overshot waterwheel. The Dutch gable, which features in a number of paintings, is on the far side of the mill. From an old postcard. *Author's collection*

Ingsdon Mill, Ilsington. Seen in September 1960. *Alan Stoyel*

Bagtor Mill, Ilsington. Overshot waterwheel by Beare. Seen from the nearby lane in August 2010

Keyberry Mill, Newton Abbot. Waterwheel at work in 1960, shortly before the mill was demolished.
Alan Stoyel

Bickley Mill, Ipplepen. Operating as the Bickley Mill Inn, in April 1996

Kingskerswell or Whitpot Mill, Kingskerswell. The overshot waterwheel. From a pre-Second World War postcard.
Author's collection

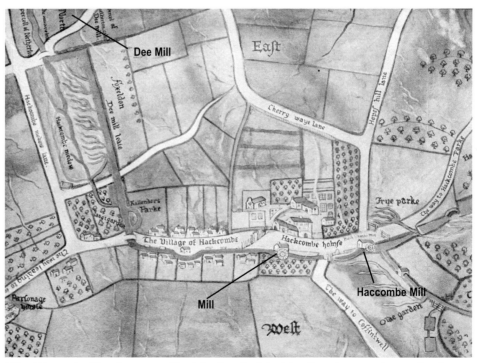

Mills at Haccombe. Map drawn on a skin, dating from the late sixteenth century, or early seventeenth century. Reproduced from a Haccombe estate sales leaflet of 1942.
Courtesy Devon Heritage Services, image reference Z18/64

Sites on streams from Kingskerswell and Marldon

Keyberry Mill, Newton Abbot
*Grain mill, demolished,
on Ford Leat/Aller Brook*
SX 870 704

Lower Bickley Mill, Ipplepen
Grain mill, now a house conversion
SX 8638 6713

Bickley Mill, Ipplepen
Grain mill, now a public house
SX 8641 6652

Compton Mill, Marldon
Grain mill
SX 8640 6614

Aller Mill, Newton Abbot
Paper mill, later a bone mill
SX 8766 6891

Kingskerswell Mill, Kingskerswell
Grain mill
SX 8755 6806

Tannery, Kingskerswell
SX 880 679

Daccombe Mill, Coffinswell
Grain mill, demolished by 1890
SX 8874 6775

Stream from Haccombe

Netherton Mill, Haccombe with Combe
Grain mill, demolished
SX 8918 7130

Home Farm, Haccombe with Combe
Farm mill
SX 8945 7039

Elizabethan mill sites, Haccombe
Probable grain or fulling mills. Dee Mill and two others by Haccombe House, possibly late sixteenth century. All long gone
SX 898 700

Stream from Charlecombe

Charlecombe Mill, Stokeinteignhead
Grain mill. House built on site circa 1920
SX 9078 7112

Stream from Stokeinteignhead

Higher Home Farm, Stokeinteignhead
Turbine which powered farm machinery including thresher, chaff cutter; electrical storage batteries
SX 9167 7034
A possible second site existed at **Paynes Court Farm**, SX 9170 7058, behind Mill Leat Farm

Mill painted by Reverend Swete in 1795. Thought to be Netherton Mill, Combeinteignhead, but was possibly Bitton Mill, near Teignmouth. Both mills have long since disappeared from the landscape. *Courtesy Devon Heritage Services, image reference 564M/F8/149*

Higher Home Farm, Stokeinteignhead
The farm here employed a turbine in the twentieth century. Seen in August 2013

Sites on the Colley Brook and Ugbrooke Stream

Abbrook pump, Kingsteignton
Waterwheel pump for ball clay industry
SX 864 747
Sandygate Mill, Kingsteignton
Grain mill, demolished in 1960s
SX 8868 0747
Oldchard, Ideford
Water pump
SX 878 770 possibly - location not known
Coombe Mill, Ideford
Grain mill; gear stripped out in 1882
SX 873 759
Ideford Mill, Ideford
Grain mill; ruined walls exist
SX 885 767

Abbrook pump
wheel, Kingsteignton.
A high breastshot fed
by a siphon. Seen in
August 1960. The
shrouds carried the
inscription
'H. BLAKE & SONS,
NEWTON ABBOT
1876'.
Alan Stoyel

Luton Mill, Bishopsteignton
*Grain mill, converted. Large diameter high
breastshot waterwheel still at work in 1888.
Massive clasp arm pit wheel still on site in 2004*
SX 9013 7700
Saw Mill, Ugbrooke Park, Chudleigh
SX 871 780
*A small hydro-electric installation has recently
been installed here*
Home Farm, Ugbrooke Park, Chudleigh
SX 8778 7819
*Leat from pond at Wapperwell (SX 8819 779)
to farm buildings: probable water power here*

Stream to Kingsteignton

Lower Mill, Kingsteignton
*Grain Mill, with overshot waterwheel in situ,
by Henry Beare, 20ft dia.*
SX 8714 7281
Town Mill, Kingsteignton
Grain Mill
SX 871 731
Higher Mill, Kingsteignton
Grain mill to 1952
SX 8717 7328
Higher Humber, Bishopsteignton
Farm mill/saw mill
SX 9002 7520

Streams to Bishopsteignton

Venn Farm, Bishopsteignton
Farm mill
SX 9254 7502

Mill on the Bitton Brook

Bitton Mill, Teignmouth
Grain mill, demolished
SX 929 733

Sandygate Mill, Kingsteignton. Seen in August 1960. Since demolished. *Alan Stoyel*

Luton Mill, Ideford in 2004. Prior to conversion

Lower Mill, Kingsteignton. Seen in 2013. It retains an overshot waterwheel

Higher Mill, Kingsteignton. Seen in August 1960, before conversion to residential use. *Alan Stoyel*

Glossary

Ball clay. Clay of high plasticity and strength used in production of pottery

Bark house. A structure for storing oak bark in the dry before being ground in a bark mill

Bark mill. A mill used to grind oak bark into powder to make tannin, used in tanning leather, until superseded by chemical processes towards the end of the nineteenth century

Bolter. A powered cylinder of woollen cloth for the production of fine flour from meal; the meal beaten against wooden bars

Breastshot wheel. A waterwheel with the water flow meeting the wheel at or near its midpoint, driven by both the impulse and the weight of water

Buddle. Pit for processing crushed metallic ores; washing away lighter wastes

Calciner. A furnace or kiln that thermally decomposes ores or, for example, flints

Cogs. Wooden teeth forming the gearing on a gear wheel

Edge-tool mill. Iron mill producing scythes, billhooks, reaping tools, spades and shovels

Eye. The hole through the centre of a millstone, sometimes the centre section of a millstone

Flat rods. Iron or wood reciprocating rods transferring power from a waterwheel to a pump in a remote mine shaft, or to other machinery some distance away

Fulling mill. Where cloth is hammered by water-powered fulling stocks in a solution of water with a fulling agent, for example urine or fuller's earth.

The stocks, usually two in a mill, compact the cloth and control its shrinkage. Known as a tucking mill in the south west

Grist. The action of grinding, or the grain to be ground. Also – a small mill for grinding people's own corn. Grist in that case means a batch of grain taken to a mill for grinding

Haematite. The mineral form of iron. Micaceous haematite contains mica

Horse gin or whim. Large circular wheel mounted on an upright shaft, operated by a horse, mule or donkey, walking a circular track to transmit power to a mine or to farm machinery

Kibble. A large bucket used in mining, primarily to carry ores to surface. To be distinguished from: Kibbler. A machine for cracking grain

Launder. An aqueduct or elevated leat

Layshaft. A secondary or intermediate transmission shaft in a mill

Leat. A man-made water channel engineered to deliver water from a weir on a river or stream, or from a spring-fed pond, to a waterwheel

Millstones. *Peak stones* were made from Millstone Grit and came from the Pennines. *Welsh stones* were cut from sandstone conglomerate. *French burr stones* came from quarries to the south-east of Paris, imported via Topsham, Dartmouth and Plymouth. By the nineteenth century the French stones were made up of segments and bound by iron bands. These stones, when correctly dressed, could remove bran in large particles and made meal that was suitable for processing as flour. *Moor stones* – locally quarried on Dartmoor, from the granite

Millwright. A craftsman who builds and maintains mills

Mortar stone. A stone on which ore was crushed by mechanically-driven stamps. Distinguished by a bowl-shaped cavity, cavities or hollows

Mould stone. Granite block with one or more recessed rectangular hollows into which molten tin was poured to be cast into ingots

Nave. Central hub or boss of a waterwheel within which the wheel's shaft is located

Overshot waterwheel. Powered by water delivered by a launder to its buckets at the top of the wheel. The weight of water in the buckets turns the wheel. The overshot wheel is the most efficient type and can work with a small stream of water

Penstock. Water controller. The sluice or 'shut' that controls water flow onto a waterwheel or turbine

Provender mill. Mill producing animal feed

Roller mill. A mill employing a series of cylindrical rollers in combination with sieves to produce fine flour

Roving. A sliver of lightly-twisted wool or cotton fibres, produced by slubbing

Saggar. A ceramic, box-like container used in the firing of pottery to enclose or protect ware in kilns

Serge. A durable twilled woollen or worsted fabric

Sett. Ground licensed to a group of mining adventurers within which minerals could be extracted

Sharps. A by-product of flour dressing; a low-grade flour used for animal feed

Shrouds. Wood or cast-iron circular frames to which buckets or paddles were fixed to form a waterwheel

Slubbing machine. Produced continuous lightly-twisted threads from carded fibre known as slubbings. Slubbing was the stage before roving and spinning into yarn

Smut machine. Machine for separating smut from wheat and for cleaning all types of grain

Spinning frame. Machine for spinning thread or yarn from wool or cotton in a mechanised way, developed by Richard Arkwright

Stamps. Water-powered upright wooden stampers, often iron-shod, worked by cams on a horizontal shaft, to crush metallic ores.
Californian stamps were more rapid in action, and the heads and lifters were made to rotate so that they wore more evenly, and they were more effective than the earlier *Cornish stamps*

Tilt or trip hammer. Water-powered (or recently electrically-powered) heavy hammer operated by cams on a shaft. Used in edge-tool mills

Tin mill. Water-powered mill for processing tin ore. A stamping mill crushed the ore; a blowing mill smelted it, using bellows worked by cams to heat a furnace

Treble mill gearing. A drive from the pitwheel via a short horizontal layshaft to a pair of gears by which a pair of millstones is driven, first noted at Sidmouth in the 1590s

Undershot waterwheel. Waterwheel driven by the impulse or force of water striking the floats or paddles at or near the bottom of the wheel

Weir. Dam built across a river to raise the water level upstream and direct the flow, usually via a sluice gate, into a leat

Worsted. Yarn made from long-fibred wool, combed so that the fibres lie parallel

References

Teign mills

Bellamarsh Mills, Kingsteignton
1   Devon County Council Sites and Monuments Register 15 September 1993; A search at the RAMM in October 2014 failed to locate Bruce Bolton's drawings
2   Photographs by Alan Stoyel, 1960
3   Western Times 2 December 1864 p 1 col 1
4   DHC – deeds, including other sites: 50M/E58-73 from 1731-1775; Sherborne Mercury 6 October 1794
5   Western Times 19 January 1850 p 8 col 6
6   Exeter Flying Post 28 September 1815 p 4 col 2; DHC – 2565A/PO51/58 of 1815-17
7   DHC – 924B/B8/5 of 1819
8   R. R. Sellman, Notes and Transcripts from the Ugbrooke Records 1981, 13, citing III/9c/1
9   Western Times 22 January 1848 p 1 col 2; 17 June 1848 p 1
10 Bishopsteignton census 1861 – HO 107 1871; census 1871 – RG9 1408 f 32 p 7
11 Western Times 2 December 1864 p 1 col 1
12 Western Times 12 October 1877 p 1 col 5; 6 April 1882 p 1 col 3
13 Western Times 23 January 1885 p 4 col 1
14 Kelly's Directory, Devonshire 1919, 1056
15 Devon County Council Sites and Monuments Register 15 September 1993; notes from MS notebook by W. H. Worth, 6 January 1927 – original in possession of Tom Greeves; visit by Alan Stoyel in 1960
16 Woodward-Nutt, ed., 2007, 23
17 Rolt, 1971, 78
18 From MS notebook by W. H. Worth – original in possession of Tom Greeves

Chudleigh Bridge Mill, Chudleigh
1   Gray, ed., 1998, 61; DHC – 564M/F6/55 and 1803Z/Z13
2   Chudleigh History Group web site, citing a deed of 1781, dated 15 January, held at East Riding of Yorkshire Archives and Records Service
3   Chudleigh census 1841 – HO107 /219/8
4   Exeter Flying Post 3 October 1844 p 3 col 7
5   Western Times 9 September 1848 p 6 cols 4 and 5
6   Chudleigh census 1851 – HO107 1870 f 398 p 1
7   Chudleigh census 1861 – RG9 1402
8   Exeter Flying Post 27 October 1875 p 7 col 2
9   Chudleigh History Group web site

Palace Mill, Chudleigh
1   Sherborne Mercury 3 March 1794 p 3
2   DHC – Chudleigh tithe apportionment, 1838
3   Chudleigh census 1851 – HO107 1870 f 398 p 4
4   Exeter Flying Post 11 March 1858 p 4 col 2; Exeter Flying Post 12 May 1859 p 1 col 3
5   Chudleigh census 1861 – RG9 1402
6   Exeter Flying Post 14 March 1877 p 7 col 6
7   R. R. Sellman, Notes and Transcriptions from the Ugbrooke Records, 1981, 68, citing IV/9A/15
8   Western Times 12 September 1884 p 1 col 4; Kingsteignton census 1891 – RG12 1700
9   Western Times 2 January 1891 p 1 col 1
10 Chudleigh census 1891 – RG12 1696 f 91 p13
11 Mid-Devon Advertiser 20 March 1897
12 Western Times 22 December 1863 p 2 col 2, death of daughter, Exeter; Winchester census 1871 – RG10 1211 f 54 p 20; Winchester census 1881 – RG11/1233; Bishop's Waltham census 1891 – RG12 941 f 34 p14; fire at Beare Mill, Crediton – Exeter and Plymouth Gazette 21 October 1897 p 4 col 2; Chudleigh census 1901 – RG13 2051
13 Kelly's Directory, Devonshire, 1902, 1065; Chudleigh History Group web site
14 Exeter & Plymouth Gazette 18 March 1910 p 5 last col
15 Chudleigh History Group web site
16 Personal communication Martin Watts 1 September 2014

Parkway Mill, Chudleigh
1   DHC – 3459M/T218a-b; Chudleigh History Group web site
2   DHC – 3329M/T1-23
3   Royal Exchange Fire Insurance Policy 71251, 23 August 1777 – Guildhall Library London
4   Sherborne Mercury, circa 5 November 1790
5   DHC – 3009A-99/PO19/210-211. Mary Causeley, 9, apprenticed to Samuel Paul Bamford, woollen manufacturer for the mills; Chudleigh History Group web site, citing Land Tax returns
6   Woolmer's Gazette 6 December 1823 p 3 col 5
7   Chudleigh History Group web site, citing Land Tax returns and 1832/36 Electoral Rolls
8   Exeter Flying Post, 11 September 1834 p 3 col 6
9   Chudleigh History Group web site, citing census returns; White's Directory, Devonshire 1850
10 Exeter Flying Post 18 January 1860 p 1 col 3
11 Chudleigh census 1861 – RG9 1402
12 Western Times 11 March 1864 p 1 col 1
13 Exeter Flying Post 13 June 1866 p 1 col 5
14 Western Times 2 July 1869 p 1 col 1

15 Chudleigh census 1861 – Farley Mills. RG9 1402; 1870 at Parkway – Chudleigh History Group; Chudleigh census 1881 – RG11 2158
16 Exeter Flying Post 27 October 1875 p 7 col 2
17 The Miller 6 October 1884
18 Chudleigh census 1891 – RG12 1696 f 91 p13; Exeter and Plymouth Gazette 6 September 1895 p 4
19 Chudleigh census 1901 – RG13 2051 f 104 p25
20 The Miller 6 May 1901; Western Times 17 May 1901 p 1 col 4
21 Mid-Devon Advertiser 25 May 1901
22 Chudleigh History Group web site

Town Mills, Chudleigh

1 Chudleigh History Group web site
2 Chudleigh History Group, citing Devon Freeholder Lists
3 Exeter Flying Post 16 August 1792; Sherborne Mercury 20 August 1792
4 Watts, 2002, 120-121
5 Chudleigh History Group web site
6 Chudleigh History Group web site, citing trade directories, Electoral Roll
7 Chudleigh History Group web site, citing Chudleigh tithe apportionment
8 Chudleigh census 1841– HO107/219/8; John's bankruptcy, etc – Western Times 9 September 1848 p 6 cols 4 and 5; Chudleigh History Group web site
9 Woolmer's Gazette 14 February 1846 p 2 col 6
10 Chudleigh History Group web site, citing fire of 30 September 1858, recorded in Weekly Express newspaper
11 Chudleigh History Group; personal communication from Martin Watts 6 June 2003
12 Chudleigh census returns 1871, 1881, 1891 and 1901; town directory 1889, 1893
13 Western Times 19 May 1893 p 4 col 2
14 Chudleigh History Group web site
15 Chudleigh History Group web site, citing South Devon Weekly Express
16 Western Morning News 9 November 1972, 8 May 1973 and 5 May 1979
17 Chudleigh History Group web site
18 Martin Watts, personal communication 4 October 2014

Waddon Barton, Chudleigh

1 Sherborne Mercury 6 January 1817; Exeter Flying Post 9 January 1817
2 Advice from Chris Cox of Higher Oxencombe Farm, 9 March 2004; from Mr Burling of Waddon Barton in 2014
3 Chudleigh History Group web site

Harcombe Mills, Chudleigh

1 DHC – 484M/T16/1-2 of 1680-81; 484M/T19/11-2 of 1681-88 and 484M/T9/1, also T10/1 of 1690.
2 DHC – 484M/T1-44, 48-9
3 DHC – 484M/T9/8
4 DHC – 484M/T1/53-66
5 Chudleigh History Group web site

Farley Mill, Chudleigh

1 DHC – 58/9 box 120/8-9
2 Western Times 2 January 1836 p 1 col 5; the leat from the Bramble Brook is shown on the Chudleigh tithe map and on the Ordnance Survey 1:2,500 map of 1888
3 Western Times 14 June 1845 p 1 col 1
4 Trade directories; Chudleigh census 1841, 1861 – RG9 1402; Exeter Flying Post 27 April 1870 p 1 col 1; Chudleigh census 1881 – RG11 2159 f 6 p 6, 1901 – RG13 2051 f 106 p 30
5 English Heritage, Swindon – NMR SC00250 Haldon Estate, 5 July 1918; Chudleigh tithe apportionment 1838
6 Chudleigh History Group web site

Hyner Mill, Hennock

1 Exeter Flying Post 5 May 1785 p 3 col 2; DHC – Z10/11/1 of 1785
2 Exeter Flying Post 18 September 1806 p 4
3 Trade directories; Hennock census 1851 – HO107 1870; 1861 – RG9 1403; 1871 – RG10 2076
4 The Miller 21 March 1898
5 Schmitz, 1980, 104

Hennock Silver Lead Mine, Hennock

1 DHC – Z10/11/14   dated 3 June 1812
2 Exeter Flying Post 29 December 1836 p 2 col 4
3 Collins, 1912, 507
4 Liverpool census 1841
5 Mining Journal 1850
6 Western Times 3 May 1851 p 6 col 3
7 Exeter Flying Post 1 July 1852 p 5 col 6
8 Exeter Flying Post 3 March 1853 p 4 col 5; DHC – Williams, Cornwall & Devon Mining Directory, second edition 1862, revised. From notes transcribed by Hugh Wilson Holman
9 Exeter Flying Post 3 June 1852 p 5 col 5
10 Exeter Flying Post 31 May 1855 p 1 col 3
11 Western Times 6 October 1855 p 1 col 3
12 Western Times 30 January 1863 p 3
13 Western Times 13 December 1862
14 Exeter & Plymouth Gazette 3 June 1864 p 3
15 Exeter & Plymouth Gazette 17 January 1868 p 1 col 3

Great Rock Mine, Hennock
1   Exeter Flying Post 31 August 1848 p 5 col 4; Western Times 15 December 1860 p 3
2   Richardson, 1995, 72; Brooks, 2004, 38, 107, 135

Pool Mill, Hennock
1   DHC – QS/DP/244, Tormorham Water Works, 1855; Exeter and Plymouth Gazette 18 April 1857 p 8 col 2
2   Hennock census 1841 – HO107/253/17 dist 16 f 4
3   Exeter Flying Post 30 June 1842 p 1 col 3
4   White's Directory of Devonshire, 1850, 472

Moorbarn, Moretonhampstead
1   DHC – Z10/7/1 of 1795
2   Dr T. A. P. Greeves 5/9/1980, worksheet. Cited in Devon C.C. Sites and Monuments Register 15/09/80.
3   Sale by FPD Savills, 13 Southernhay West, Exeter, in 2003

Frank Mills mine, Christow
1   DHC – 867B/MS2-3 of 1852; 867B/MS5 of 1855
2   Exeter Flying Post 29 November 1855 p 5 col 5
3   Hamilton Jenkin, 2005, 138; Schmitz, 1980, 105
4   Western Times 31 May 1864 p 2 last col; Christow census 1861 – RG9 1391 f 38 p 12; Exeter & Plymouth Gazette 12 February 1869, citing the South Devon Gazette
5   Western Times 18 July 1876 p 7
6   Western Times 6 August 1880 p 1 col 5
7   Schmitz, 1980, 105-106; Richard W. M. Nance and R. Damian Nance, A Survey of Engine Houses on the Mines of South Devon, Bulletin of the Peak District Mines Historical Society, 13, No 2, Winter 1996, 109-122

Shuttamoor Mine, Christow
1   DHC – 867B/MS6 of 1856
2   Brooks, 2004, 164 - 166
3   Western Times 18 February 1910 p 12 col 3
4   Brooks, 2004, 164 - 166

Wheal Exmouth, Christow
1   Exeter Flying Post 28 July 1853 p 3 col 4; Exeter & Plymouth Gazette 14 August 1852 p 5 col 4; White's Devonshire Directory, 1850 – Christow entry
2   Cornwall Record Office – H/1/43/386 of 1853; Wheal Adams and Wheal Exmouth were linked underground by 1853 – Exeter & Plymouth Gazette 23 April 1853 p 5 last col
3   Kenneth Brown, Prestongrange 70-in Cornish Engine – A Myth Exploded, Journal of the Trevithick Society, 1982
4   Exeter Flying Post 16 April 1862 p 1 col 2

5   Brown, op cit, 1982
6   Western Times 6 August 1880 p 1 col 5
7   English Heritage entry for engine house

Ashton Mills, Ashton
1   DHC – Pearse Box 2/4/1/9
2   Guildhall Library, London – Sun Fire Insurance Policy 503854, 19 April 1785
3   DHC – 1693M/TL
4   Sherborne Mercury 31 December 1804
5   Sherborne Mercury 20 July 1807 p 4 col 5; Exeter Flying Post 1 September 1808 p 1
6   Western Times 1 August 1835 p 3 col 1
7   Ashton census – HO107 1867 f 467 p 17
8   Western Times 26 August 1861 p 1 col 5
9   Western Times 27 November 1866 p 1 col 2
10 Western Times 14 March 1871 p 1; Ashton census 1911 – RG14 12633 sch 1; Kelly's Directory, Devonshire, 1919, 1056; Notes from MS notebook by W.H. Worth (visit 6 January 1927) – original now in possession of Tom Greeves
11 Department of the Environment. List of Buildings of Special Architectural or Historic Interest. District of Teignbridge. Parishes of Ashton, etc. 1988, 21
12 Place Barton, Ashton – painting at Royal Albert Memorial Museum, Exeter, 1826 - ref 46/1956/6; Western Times 17 March 1855 p 1

Christow Mill, Christow
1   DHC – Z10/19/22-23, 35 of 1814 and 1832; DHC – 62/9/2/Box5/41, October 1867
2   Christow census 1851 – HO107 1867 f 432 p 40; DHC - 62/9/2/Box5/41 of 17 October 1867; Exeter & Plymouth Gazette 20 September 1867 p 1 col 2
3   Trade directory; Christow census 1871 – RG10 2058 f 44 p 27
4   Western Times 26 July 1901 p 4 col 2
5   Western Times 9 November 1921 p 3 col 1
6   Western Times 6 March 1925 p 2 col 3
7   Stags sale notice, 2001
8   www.abihiggins.co.uk
9   Abi Higgins, personal communication 12 November 2014

Teign Valley Barytes Mine, Bridford
1   Adit now web site
2   Exeter Flying Post 28 July 1853 p 3 col 4
3   Exeter and Plymouth Gazette Daily Telegram 21 March 1870 p 1 col 2
4   Adit-now web site
5   Exeter and Plymouth Gazette 14 September 1883 p 5;

Christopher J. Schmitz, The development and decline of the Devon Barytes industry, 1875-1958, Trans. Devonshire Association 109, 1977, 117-133

6 Bridford census 1891 – RG12 1685; 1901 – RG13 2039 f 104 p 8

7 DHC – 4634M-0 from 1938 to 1958.
Notes by Col. J. V. Ramsden; a director of the Devonshire Baryta Company; Adit-now web site; Christopher J. Schmitz, The development and decline of the Devon Barytes industry, 1875-1958, Trans. Devonshire Association 109, (1977) 117-133

8 Hall, 1990, 103

Stone Farm, Bridford

1 Exeter and Plymouth Gazette 29 March 1895 p 1 col 2

2 Devon and Exeter Gazette 15 April 1897 p 4 col 6; Bridford census 1901 – RG13 2039 f 104 p 8

3 Exeter and Plymouth Gazette 7 May 1920 p 2 col 3

Stone Mill, Bridford

1 Bridford tithe apportionment 1840, items 1212, 1214 etc; Christow census 1851 – HO107 1867; 1861 – RG9 1391 f 48 p 31

2 Western Times 25 May 1866 p 1 col 1

3 Christow census 1871 – RG10 2058 f 22 p 14

4 Western Times 9 August 1889 p 1 col 2

5 Christow census 1891 – RG12 1685

6 Western Times 7 September 1893 p 8 col 6

7 Western Times 31 August 1906 p 13 col 2

8 Exeter and Plymouth Gazette 4 October 1922 p 3 col 5

Bridford Mill, Bridford

1 DHC – 1914Z/T6 of 1753

2 Guildhall Library, London – Sun Fire Insurance Policy 430278, 27 June 1780

3 Exeter Flying Post 29 September 1825 p 4 col 4

4 Woolmer's Gazette 5 May 1827 p 1 col 3

5 Woolmer's Gazette 5 November 1836 p 2 col 6

6 Exeter Flying Post 31 January 1833 p 1 col 2; Bridford tithe apportionment; Woolmer's Gazette 17 July 1841 p 1 col 1

7 Woolmer's Gazette 16 November 1850 p 1 col 1

8 Bridford census 1851 – HO 107 1867 f 402 p 19

9 Western Times 6 February 1889 p 2 col 1

10 Bridford census 1891 – RG12 1685 f 8 p 10

11 Bridford census 1901 – RG13 2039 f 104 p 8

12 Kelly's Directory of Devonshire 1908, 1088-1090; Bridford census 1911 – RG14 12634 sh 47; Western Times 16 July 1921 p 2 col 1

13 From MS notebook by W. H. Worth (visits in January 1927 and March 1934) – original in possession of Tom Greeves - see also Surridge, 1950

Birch Aller Mine, Bridford

1 Exeter Flying Post 31 May 1855 p 1 col 3; Christopher J. Schmitz, The Teign Valley Silver-Lead Mines, 1806-1880, Northern Mine Research Society, 1980, 107

2 Exeter Flying Post 24 April 1851 p 8 col 5; 3 June 1852 p 5 col 5

3 Western Times 6 October 1855 p 1 col 3

Sowton Mill, Dunsford

1 Ninth Report of Committee on Devonshire Records, Trans. Devonshire Association, 1899, 126

2 DHC – 4572 A-99/PO 7/260 of 1757

3 Sherborne Mercury 18 January 1796

4 Dunsford Tithe Apportionment, 1837, items 1300-1310; Dunsford census 1841 – HO107 263/6; census 1851 – HO107 1867 f 389 p 10

5 Western Times 19 April 1872 p 4 col 2; Dunsford census 1871 – RG10 2056 f 28 p 10

6 Dunsford census 1891 – RG12 1684 f 5 p 4; Western Times 16 August 1895 p 4 col 2

7 Western Times 12 May 1899 p 4 col 1

8 Dunsford census 1901 – RG13 2039; Kelly's Directory of Devonshire 1908, 1088-1090

9 Western Times 6 July 1918 p 3

10 Kelly's Directory, Devonshire, 1919, 1056

11 DOE/HHR: Dunsford 4/9/1986, 24, quoted in Devon County Council Sites and Monuments Register 24/11/89; Notes from MS notebook by W.H. Worth – original now in possession of Tom Greeves

12 Western Times 19 October 1945 p 1 col 6

13 TRESOC –-Totnes Renewable Energy Society web site

Wheal Lawrence, Dunsford

1 Exeter Flying Post 7 July 1853 p 4 col 5; DHC – 1926B/FU/E6/17 of 1852-53

Wheal Anna Maria, Dunsford

1 Western Times 18 September 1847 p 1 col 1 [Shareholders' meeting]; A. K. Hamilton Jenkin, Mines of Devon. North and East of Dartmoor. Devon Library Services, 1981, 167-169; Mining Journal July 1850

2 Dunsford census 1851 – HO 107 1807 f 367 p 21; Hennock census 1841 – HO 107/253 bk 15 d14 f 7 p 10; Redruth census 1861 – RG9 1579

3 DHC – 1926B/FU/E6/17

4 Exeter Flying Post 7 July 1853 p 4 col 5

Dunsford Mills, Dunsford

1. Royal Exchange Fire Insurance Policy 74807, 19 January 1779; DHC – Fulford Estate rent accounts 1799-1800
2. London Gazette 1-4 October 1803
3. Royal Exchange Fire Insurance Policy 214067, 4 February 1805
4. DHC - 4572 A-99/PO 5/35-36 [Mary Baxter, apprenticed 1818]; Exeter Flying Post 5 September 1839 p 2 col 5
5. Dunsford census 1851 – HO107 1807 f 368 p 23
6. DHC - 1926B/FU/E6/19
7. Western Times 26 September 1857 p 1 col 2
8. DHC - 1926 B/FU/E/6/19
9. Western Times 16 March 1880 p 1 col 2
10. Western Times [prob] 25 October 1881 p 4 col 1; Western Times 12 January 1883 p 1 col 1
11. Western Times 5 August 1891 p 2 col 1
12. Dunsford census 1901 – RG13 2039
13. Exeter and Plymouth Gazette 29 August 1902 p 1 col 6
14. Exeter and Plymouth Gazette 24 December 1902 p 4 col 5
15. Exeter and Plymouth Gazette 28 July 1903 p 4 col 2; Kelly's Directory of Devonshire 1908, 1088-1090
16. Exeter and Plymouth Gazette 8 September 1930 p 3 col 4
17. Notes from MS notebook by W. H. Worth – original now in possession of Tom Greeves; Bond, c 1997, 24

Iron Mills, Dunsford

1. English Heritage entry; Harris, 1992, 124
2. Dunsford Tithe Apportionment 1837, items 1046, 1047. Dunsford census 1841 – HO107/263/6 dst 1 f 5 p 4; White's Devonshire Directory, 1850
3. Dunsford census 1851 – HO107 1867 f 368 p 22; 1861 – RG9 1390 f 4 p 2
4. Western Times 13 October 1891 p 8 col 5
5. Western Times 20 May 1892 p 4 col 1
6. Dunsford census 1901 – RG13 2039
7. Western Times 5 June 1931 p 1 col 6; 18 September 1931 p 2 col 2
8. Notes from MS notebook by W. H. Worth – original in possession of Tom Greeves
9. Western Daily Press 28 May 2013
10. Department of the Environment/HHR: Dunsford 4/9/1986, 15, cited in Devon County Council Sites and Monuments Register 24 November 1989

Doccombe Mill, Moretonhampstead

1. DHC – 2160A/PO 788 and 1160A/PO 807a of 1825
2. DHC – Moretonhampstead tithe apportionment
3. Rootsweb site – http://archiver.rootsweb.ancestry.com/th/read/HAMLYN/2010-03/1270077720

4. Western Times 26 June 1858 p 4 col 2
5. Moretonhampstead census 1861 – RG9 1404
6. Western Times 3 October 1873 p 7 col 1
7. Exeter and Plymouth Gazette 4 January 1877 p 3 col 3
8. Devon County Council – HER records
9. Exeter & Plymouth Gazette 25 August1944 p 2

Mill site by the Teign, Moretonhampstead

1. 1639 Survey of Manor of Moretonhampstead, Hambleden Archives, Museum of English Rural Life, Reading

Clifford Farm, Moretonhampstead

1. Sale 1928 – English Heritage, Swindon NMR – SC00257
2. DHC – 1508M E/MP/Moretonhampstead plans 2

Weir Mill, Drewsteignton

1. DHC – 7525 Greener papers, box 1
2. Exeter Flying Post 10 January 1799 p 1 col 2
3. Ancestry web site message boards
4. Exeter Flying Post 23 May 1833 p 3 col 6
5. From Ancestry web site message boards; Hittesleigh census 1841
6. DHC – 7525 Greener papers, tithe apportionment
7. Woolmer's Gazette 11 September 1841 p 3 col 6
8. White's Directory, Devonshire, 1850; Drewsteignton census 1861; Morris & Co, Directory 1870; Western Times 4 March 1887 p 1 col 2
9. Western Times 29 April 1890 p 1 col 3
10. Exeter Flying Post 3 May 1890
11. Devon and Exeter Gazette 21 May 1897 p 4 col 7
12. Devon and Exeter Gazette 10 May 1901 p 1 col 6; Notes from MS notebook by W. H. Worth – original in possession of Tom Greeves, Tavistock
13. Visit by the author with Sue and Martin Watts, 31 October 2014
14. Photographs by Donald W. Muggeridge taken in 1941-1943, and personal communication with Martin Watts, September 2014
15. Western Morning News 23 March 2002; see also DHC – 547B/P3243 of 1933

Narracott and Lower Budbrook, Drewsteignton

1. Western Times 14 June 1889 p 1 col 5
2. Exeter and Plymouth Gazette 30 May 1924 p 5 col 2

Fingle Mills, Moretonhampstead

1. 1639 Survey of Manor of Moretonhampstead, Hambleden Archives, Museum of English Rural Life, Reading; DHC – 4855M/F1 of 1747

2 Elisabeth Stanbrook, Fingle Mill: the ruin among the trees, Dartmoor Magazine 21, 1990, citing Land tax lists
3 Guildhall Library, London – Sun Fire Insurance Policy 459911, 10 May 1782
4 Moretonhampstead History Society web site
5 Exeter Flying Post 21 October 1841 p 3 last col – a bay mare had been stolen or strayed from the mills; Moretonhampstead census 1851; Billings Directory 1857; Moretonhampstead census 1871 – RG10 2078; Western Times 7 November 1890 p 5 col 5
6 Exeter and Plymouth Gazette 5 September 1840 p 3 col 1 – marriage Gorwyn and Brely; Harrod's Devonshire Directory, 1878; Elisabeth Stanbrook article 1990
7 Harris, 1992, 210; T. Greeves, 26/03/1984, *Mill* (Worksheet). Site visit 23 March 1984; personal communication – Martin Watts

Castle Drogo Turbine House, Moretonhampstead
1 English Heritage and Heritage Gateway web sites citing:
- National Trust, 1982, Castle Drogo (Leaflet)
- Harris, W. B., 1995, Hydro-Electricity in Devon: Past, Present and Future
- Chitty, G., 2000, Electric Power Generation
- Watts, M., 2005, Archaeological recording for the National Trust (Report - Survey).
Also: Notes from MS notebook by W. H. Worth (visit March 1934) – original in possession of Tom Greeves

Veet Mill, Drewsteignton
1 Greener collection DHC – 7525, box 1, items 107-109 etc, Drewsteignton Overseers from 1644
2 Greener collection DHC – 7525, box 1
3 Drewsteignton tithe apportionment; DHC – Drewsteignton cuttings file, item for 1878
4 DHC – 2165 A/PO 1087 1826; – 7525 Greener papers
5 White's Directory Devonshire 1850; Drewsteignton 1851 census – HO107 1885 f 585 p 34; 1861 census – RG9 1468;
6 DHC – Drewsteignton cuttings file, item for 1878
7 Drewsteignton 1871 census – RG10 2154 f 66 p 6; Western Times 5 December 1877 p 3 col 4; Woodbury 1891 census – RG12 1677
8 Western Times 8 November 1889 p 1 col 1
9 Exeter and Plymouth Gazette 31 August 1894 p 4 col 2
10 Exeter and Plymouth Gazette 31 May 1895 p 3 col 6
11 Department of Environment, 1988, Drewsteignton (List of Buildings of Architectural or Historic Interest)

Mill Farm, Whiddon Down, Drewsteignton
1 DHC – 7525 Greener papers, box 1
2 Morris & Co, Directory, 1870; Drewsteignton census 1871 – RG10 2154 f 73 p 19
3 Western Times 28 April 1893 p 8 col 4
4 Visit by author circa 1998
5 White's Directory, Devonshire

Uppacott, Moretonhampstead
1 Western Times 1 March 1851 p 5 col 5
2 DHC – D1508M/Maps and plans/Moreton/Plans 1
3 Ordnance Survey map, sheet 90.2, of 1885
4 Western Times 15 April 1908 p 2
5 English Heritage, Swindon – NMR ref SC00257

Whiddon Park, Chagford
1 Exeter and Plymouth Gazette 23 July 1897 p 1 col 1
2 DHC – 7157/M/9 of 1921
3 Western Times 18 February 1944 p 5 col 5
4 English Heritage – Gateway web site

Sandy Park Mill, Chagford
1 DHC – 5296-3 of 12 December 1834
2 Western Times 1 August 1835 p 2 col 3
3 Exeter Flying Post 23 May 1850 p 1 col 2
4 Western Times 24 December 1880 p 4 col 1
5 Chagford census 1881 – RG11 2225
6 Western Times 25 September 1903 p 1 col 6
7 Western Times 4 September 1908 p 10 col 1
8 Kelly's Directory, Devonshire, 1919, 1065
9 Harris, 1992, 192-3; Mill End Hotel web site – http://millendhotel.com/the-hotel/history/
10 Heritage Gateway web site; see also DHC – 1695M/EA10 – Sandy Park Mill - receipt for wheat, 1885; Notes from MS notebook by W. H. Worth (visits December 1926 and March 1934) – original in possession of Tom Greeves

Furlong Mill, Drewsteignton
1 Exeter Flying Post 28 July 1869 p 1 col 1; Western Times 28 April 1876 p 1 col 1
2 Exeter Flying Post 12 May 1880 p 1 col 3; Exeter and Plymouth Gazette 4 September 1903 p 2 col 3
3 Martin Watts, personal communication 4 October 2014

Rushford Wood tin workings, Chagford
1   Mike Passmore, Tinworking in Rushford Wood, Chagford, citing Stannary Court records of 1442, DTRG Newsletter, 19, July 2000, 4,
2   Hayter-Hames, 2004, 95
3   Tom Greeves, personal communication 7 September 2014. Its status as a mill was confirmed by him in March 1990

Sandsgate Mill, Chagford
1   Visit by Tom Greeves 20 May 1989

Great Week Consols, Chagford
1   Bill Radcliffe, Field Trip Report – Mines near Chagford, DTRG Newsletter 36, January 2009, 12-13
2   DHC – 4930 B/T/C/78 & 79; Census, Islington, London, 1911 – RG14; Piece: 844
3   Western Times 25 October 1887 p 7 col 2
4   Hamilton Jenkin, 2005, 108, citing D. B. Broughton, Western Morning News 27 February 1961, Dines p 750.
5   Bill Radcliffe, Field Trip Report. Mines near Chagford, DTRG Newsletter 36, January 2009, 12-13; Atkinson et al, 1978, 48
6   Western Times 21 April 1903 p 1 col 3; A K Hamilton Jenkin, Mines of Dartmoor, Landmark Publishing, 2005, 108; DHC – 1695M add2/B3/2
    See also D. G. Broughton, Tin Working in the Eastern District of the Parish of Chagford, Devon, Proc. Geologists' Association, 78, Pt. 3, 1967, 447-462.
7   Norman J. G. Pounds, ed., The Parliamentary Survey of the Duchy of Cornwall Part II, Devon & Cornwall Record Society New Series, 27, 239-241

Rushford Barton, Chagford
1   Western Times 6 March 1868 p 1 col 3

Rushford Mill, Chagford
1   Hayter-Hames, 2004, 98
2   DHC – 1429A-99/PO 148/153 and 600-601 of 1792 and 1818
3   Exeter Flying Post 7 June 1849 p 1 col 1
4   DHC – 1429A-99/PO 148/657-658 of 1829; Western Times 20 September 1935 p 1 last col
5   White's Directory Devonshire 1850; Exeter Flying Post 30 August 1855 p 1; Hayter-Hames, 1981, 77
6   Morris's Directory 1870
7   Chagford census 1881 – RG11 2225; census 1891 – RG12 1756 f 37 p 1
8   Exeter and Plymouth Gazette 12 March 1895 p 3 col 3
9   Western Times 14 June 1935 p 4 col 4
10 Western Times 1 May 1936 p 15 col 3

11 Notes from MS notebook by W. H. Worth – (Visited December 1926 and March 1934) – original in possession of Tom Greeves
12 Harris, 1992, 193; DHC – Yeo Mill accounts, 3693M/B3 p 296
13 Exeter and Plymouth Gazette 16 November 1894 p 7 col 4; Western Times 29 November 1946 p 7 col 3

Woollen Mills, Chagford
1   Sue Price and Jean Rhodes, From Wool to Electricity, in Aspects of Devon History: people, places and landscapes, Devon History Society, 2012, 320-322
2   Hoskins, 1992, 125
3   Price and Rhodes, 2012, 322, citing builder William Stone's estimate book (in private hands); Rice, 2002, 41-42
4   Exeter Flying Post 21 August 1828
5   Moore, 1829, 560
6   Gill, ed., 1970, 123; Harris, 1992, 119-120
7   Exeter and Plymouth Gazette 25 October 1851 p 1 col 3
8   Bodman, 2008, 97; Harris, 1992, 119-120
9   Western Times 10 September 1867 p 4 col 2; Morris's Directory 1870 – Chagford entry
10 Western Times 7 April 1874 p 8 col 4
11 Western Times 17 June 1882 p 1 col 3
12 G. H. Reed papers in private hands
13 Harris, 1992, 119-120; Hayter-Hames, 2004, 109; Kelly's Directory 1893; Price and Rhodes, 2012, 330-332; Western Renewable Energy web site
14 Notes from MS notebook by W. H. Worth (visited in December 1926 and March 1934) – original in possession of Tom Greeves
15 See 13 for references

Millpond, Chagford
1   English Heritage – listed buildings in Chagford. Listed Grade II, listing no: 1106198

Moorlands, Mill Street, Chagford
1   Hayter-Hames, 2004, 109, 90
2   Dartmoor National Park Authority entry for Chagford; English Heritage – listed buildings in Chagford. Listed Grade II, listing no: 1106149

Holy Street Mill, Chagford
1   Hayter-Hames, 2004, 19; Harris, 1986, 192
2   Martin Watts, personal communication, October 2008
3   DHC – Lithograph by William Spreat, 1884 - ref SC0333
    Also painting at Royal Albert Memorial Museum by Spreat
4   Exeter Flying Post 26 April 1849, p 1; Western Times 30 November 1850 p 1 col 2

5 'Holly [sic] Street Mill, Chagford', watercolour by Charles Frederick Williams, 1868, Southampton City Art Gallery, accession number 791 and discussion with Martin Watts 1 September 2014
6 Chagford census 1851 – HO107 1885; Peter Bushell, 'Holy Street Manor', c 1986. Copy of typescript report in the possession of Tom Greeves, provided by the then owner of Holy Street, Sally Meadows
7 Notes from MS notebook by W. H. Worth – original in possession of Tom Greeves
8 English Heritage entry
9 Martin Watts, personal communication, 25 October 2008
10 Harris, 1986, 192
11 Martin Watts, personal communication, October 2008; Western Renewable Energy web site
12 Michael Moss, personal communication, September 2014

West Coombe, Chagford
1 Western Times 15 July 1873 p 1 col 2
2 Exeter Flying Post 14 August 1878 p 1 col 3
3 Exeter Flying Post 15 September 1880 p 1 col 3

Outer Down tin blowing mill, Chagford
1 R. Hansford Worth, 1953, 292; previously in TDA, lix, 343; English Heritage entry, citing i) Field Investigator's comments – F1 JGB 2 February1978, ii) CBA Research Report (T.A.P. Greeves) 40, 1981, p 94

Dartmoor Sanatorium turbine house, Chagford
1 Tom Greeves, personal communication 23 October 2014; Notes from MS notebook by W. H. Worth (visited in 1926 and 1927) – original in possession of Tom Greeves

Yeo Mill, Chagford
1 Hayter-Hames, 2004, 95
2 DHC – 3963M/B3-4 – Yeo Saw Mills, Perryman family, 1868-1966
3 Martin Watts, personal communication, 20 December 1999
4 Chagford census 1851 – HO107 1885 f 553 p 15
5 Martin Watts, personal communication, 20 December 1999
6 Notes from MS notebook by W. H. Worth (visited in December 1926 and again in March 1934) – original in possession of Tom Greeves
7 Chagford census 1891 – RG12 1756 f 46 p 4
8 Western Times 31 January 1936 p 8 cols 6 and 7
9 Western Times 18 December 1942 p 5 cols 6 and 7
10 DHC – 3963/B 3/4

Thornworthy tin blowing mill, Chagford
1 R. Hansford Worth, The Dartmoor Blowing Houses, Trans. Devonshire Association, 72, 1940, 213; revised dimensions from Tom Greeves, personal communication, 19 August 2014

Southill tin blowing mills, Chagford
1 Murray Oates and Tom Greeves, Walk along Southill Leat and to Blacksmith's Shop Blowing Mill, 20 April 2013, DTRG Newsletter 45, 12-13
2 Personal communication from Tom Greeves, 14 December 2013
3 Western Times 26 June 1847 p 1 col 4

Small hydro-electric schemes on the South and North Teign rivers
1 Information from Michael Moss 11 September 2014; Advice from Chris Elliot of WRE Ltd, 29 September 2014, re Gidleigh Park

Blacksmith's Shop/Fayrecombe, Dartmoor Forest
1 Tom Greeves, Fayrecombe – A 15th Century Record for 'Blacksmith's Shop' Tin Blowing Mill (Teignhead), DTRG Newsletter 44, January 2013, 9

Old Gidleigh Mill, Gidleigh
1 C. A. Howis Croxford, A Walkabout Guide to Gidleigh, Gidleigh Parochial Church Council 1988
2 DHC – diagrammatic map of 1699 prepared for court case – DD/35548
3 DHC – DD/35547

New Gidleigh Mill, Gidleigh
1 Lynette Costello, The Bradford Pool Case, Trans. Devonshire Association, 113, 1981, 61-64, citing DHC – DD/35547, DD/35548, DD/35539, DD/35534
2 DHC – 1306B/TL4-5 lease from c 1716; 1306B/TL17-18 conveyance 1726; assignment 1737 – 1360B/TL9

Blackaton, Throwleigh
1 Exeter and Plymouth Gazette 22 September 1944 p 1 col 7
2 Information from Michael Moss 11 September 2014

Wonson Mill, Throwleigh
1 DHC – 4930 B/T/T/1
2 DHC – 4930 B/T/T/2
3 DHC – 4930 B/T/T/3, 4-5, 6
4 DHC – 4930 B/T/T/23 of 1794; 4930 B/T/T/12, 13-18 of 1806; Throwleigh tithe map and apportionment, 1840.
5 Varwell, 1938, 47

Wyndhurst, Throwleigh
1   Paget, 2006, 159

Frog Mill, South Tawton
1   Ethel Lega-Weekes, Neighbours of North Wyke, Trans. Devonshire Association, 33, 1901, 452
2   Varwell, 1938, 45
3   Exeter and Plymouth Gazette 3 November 1860 p 1 col 2
4   DHC – 3212A/PO 113/2/59 of 1828. William took on an apprentice, James Fewins, aged 9; South Tawton census 1841 – HO107/265/1 dist 10 f 4 p 2; 1871 – RG10 2153 f 118 p 7; 1881 – RG11 2224 f 111 p 7
5   DHC – 67/5/2/1 item 961; 67/5/2/2 item 838 of 1872; 67/5/2/3 – item 973 of 1879
6   South Tawton census 1891 – RG12 1755 f 99 p 7; 1901 – RG13 2126 f 99 p 5
7   Exeter and Plymouth Gazette 12 March 1909 p 2 col 2; J. S. Browning, John's son, 30, was living on his own means in 1891 – Hittesleigh census RG12 1759 f 88 p 5
8   Exeter and Plymouth Gazette 24 February 1911 p 2 col 4

Mill Farm, East Week, Throwleigh
1   Radford, 2000, 77
2   DHC – Throwleigh tithe map and apportionment
3   Throwleigh census 1841 – HO107/265/20 dist 13 f 5 p 5
4   Ethel Lega-Weekes, Neighbours of North Wyke, Trans. Devonshire Association, 33, 1901, 455
5   Western Times 9 August 1907 p 1 col 5

West Gooseford Farm, South Tawton
1   Visit by the author, March 1997
2   Exeter Flying Post 10 November 1853 p 1 col 1
3   Western Times, 19 May 1908 p 5 col 3
4   Exeter and Plymouth Gazette 26 January 1909 p 6 col 2; Manaton census 1911 – RG14 12721 sch 10
5   Exeter and Plymouth Gazette 2 February 1909 p 3 col 3
6   The Cornishman 25 May 1911 p 1 col 3
7   Exeter and Plymouth Gazette 28 March 1918 p 5 last col
8   Western Times 18 January 1924 p 11

Bradford Tinwork, Drewsteignton
1   Advice by Tom Greeves in an email, December 2013; paper by Michael Moss of Murchington, forthcoming
2   DHC – DD/35547. Statement by George Burgoyne in 1698
3   Lynette M. Costello. The Bradford Pool Case. Trans. Devonshire Association 113, 1981, 59-77
4   T. A. P. Greeves, Great Courts or Parliaments of Devon Tinners 1474-1786, Trans. Devonshire Association, 119, 1987, 145-167

5   Dave Brewer, The Gidleigh Mill and Bradford Tinworks Leats, Part One. Dartmoor Magazine 27, Summer 1992, 8-9; Part 2, Dartmoor Magazine, 28, Autumn 1992, 24-26
6   DHC – DD/35534
7   Lynette M. Costello, The Bradford Pool Case, Trans. Devonshire Association 113, 1981, 59-77
8   Tom Greeves, 2006, comments seen on a web site
9   Hamilton Jenkin, 2005, 106-107, citing Mining Journal 27 February 1847, 26 August 1848, 10 March 1849; Western Times 17 March 1849 p 7 col 4

Leat to South Zeal
1   Ethel Lega-Weekes, Neighbours of North Wyke, Trans. Devonshire Association, 33, 1901, 450; Notes from Michael Moss of Murchington, 15 September 2014
2   Ethel Lega-Weekes, Neighbours of North Wyke, Trans. Devonshire Association, 33, 1901
3   M. W. Beresford and H. P. R. Finberg, 1973, 98

Ramsley Copper Mine, South Zeal
1   Hamilton Jenkin, 2005, 103-105; Tom Greeves, Ramsley Copper Mine, South Zeal, Devon, Archive 7, September 1995, 59 et seq.

Zeal Mill, South Zeal, South Tawton
1   Rippon et al, 2009, 141
2   Notes from Michael Moss of Murchington, 15 September 2014
3   Exeter Flying Post 2 February 1776 p 3 col 4
4   Etching by William Prout, 1811. DHC – SC2694
5   South Tawton census 1841 – HO107/265/3/ dist. 12, f 12, p19
6   Ethel Lega-Weekes, Neighbours of North Wyke, Trans. Devonshire Association, 33, 1901, 455
7   Ethel Lega-Weekes, Neighbours of North Wyke, Trans. Devonshire Association, 33, 1901, 450-451, 455; Note from Michael Moss of Murchington, 15 September 2014; DHC – South Tawton tithe map, 1847, and tithe apportionment 1844: Tucking Mill (field) item 983; Blowing Mills, item 931
8   Peter Watson of Okehayes Nursery, personal communication 21 October 2014

South Tawton Mill, South Tawton
1   SHC – DD/WY/47/3/49
2   Exeter Flying Post 24 August 1815 p 2 col 3
3   Western Times 10 July 1858 p 1 col 1
4   South Tawton census 1871; Exeter Flying Post 25 August 1875 p 1 col 4
5   Notes by the present owner, Alan Wright, in February 2009, citing Kelly's Directory 1930

6 Visit by the author in April 1998 and in 1999; Notes by Martin Watts on a visit on 20 August 2003

7 Notes by the present owner, Alan Wright, in February 2009

Higher and Lower Quarries, South Tawton
1 DHC – South Tawton tithe map 1847, item 1505
2 Exeter Flying Post 26 May 1869 p 1col 1; Woolmer's Gazette 31 July 1874 p 1 col 5
3 Western Times 2 May 1879 p 1 col 1

Bovey

Jewsbridge Mill, Tracebridge
1 Rex Wailes, *Water-driven Mills for Grinding Stone,* Trans. Newcomen Society, Vol 39, 1966-67, 95-119
2 Western Times 3 June 1890 p 8 col 5; Western Times 28 October 1890 p 8 col 7
3 Exeter and Plymouth Gazette 12 November 1890 p 5 col 2
4 Rex Wailes, *Water-driven Mills for Grinding Stone*, Trans. Newcomen Society, Vol 39, 1966-67, 95-119
5 Ordnance Survey maps 1: 2,500 for 1905 and 1933
6 Woodward-Nutt, ed., 2007, 76-77; but check Cheddleton opening times at:
http://people.exeter.ac.uk/akoutram/cheddleton-mill/
Mosty Lea Mill:
http://www.bbc.co.uk/stoke/content/articles/2009/07/08/mosty_lea_mill_feature.shtml
7 Hemery, 1991, 114

Little Bovey, Bovey Tracey
1 Tregoning, 1993, 38
2 DHC – Bovey Tracey tithe map 1840

Bovey Pottery, Bovey Tracey
1 Hoskins, 1992, 143; Peter J. Weddell and Keith Westcott, The Bovey Tracey Pottery Kilns, Devon Archaeology Society Proceedings 44, 1986, 143-162
2 Bovey Tracey Town Council web site 2013
3 William Crossing – newspaper article circa 1900
4 The Bovey Pottery Company Limited – www.kalendar.demon.co.uk/pountbovey.htm
5 Exeter Flying Post 19 July 1804
6 Western Times 18 January 1850, p 8 cols 4-6: article on pottery
7 Exeter Flying Post 6 August 1835 p 3 col 5, p 2 col 3

8 DHC - L1508/Maps and plans/Bovey Tracey/A1
9 Western Times 18 January 1850, p 8 cols 4-6: article on pottery
10 Tregoning, 1983, 71
11 DHC – 4622M/T/16; Western Times 3 June 1890 p 8 col 5
12 DHC – 67/5/2/1 items 601-4
13 Bovey Tracey census 1881 – RG11 2158 f 84 p 37
14 Tregoning, 1983, 71-2
15 Exeter and Plymouth Gazette 19 November 1894 p 4 col 5; 3 January 1925, p 5 col 5; kalendar.demon.co.uk/pountbovey.htm
16 Tregoning, 1983
17 Jim Black, engineer to the Bovey Pottery Co, 1952-1956, in a meeting with the author, 6 September 2014
18 The People's Guardian 20 February 1957, citing an article in the Pottery Gazette; Dartmoor Preservation Association web site
19 Les Breney, personal communication, 30 June 2014; Jim Black, personal communication, 14 July 2014

Yarner Copper Mine, Bovey Tracey
1 DHC – 924B/E1/9
2 Exeter Flying Post 20 May 1858 p 5
3 Hamilton Jenkin, 2005, 129, citing Mining Journal 1857-1866 and Geolog: Mem. Newton Abbot, 1913
4 Exeter and Plymouth Gazette 15 September 1865 p 1 col 1
5 Lander, 2012

Bovey Mills, Bovey Tracey
1 DHC – D1/44/5, 7-9
2 DHC – D1/44/7
3 Sherborne Mercury 4 January 1779
4 Crowdy et al, 2001
5 Western Times 10 October 1835 p 1 col 1; DHC – Bovey Tracey tithe apportionment 1839, item 1214; Exeter Flying Post 10 September 1840 p 1 col 1; Exeter & Plymouth Gazette 16 January 1841 p 1 col 2; Exeter Flying Post 10 February 1842 p 2 col 4
6 Western Times 12 April 1856 p 1 col 1; Bovey Tracey census 1861 – RG9 1403; Western Times 6 April 1861 p 1 col 1
7 Bovey Tracey census 1871 – RG10 2077 f 45 p 21; Hennock census, 1861
8 Bovey Tracey census 1871; Western Times 2 June 1863 p 1 col 2

9   Bovey Tracey census 1881 – RG11 2158
10   Exeter and Plymouth Gazette 2 December 1904 p 1 col 1
11   Bovey Tracey census 1911 – RG14 12708
12   Tregoning 1989, 25; Western Times 27 September 1916
13   Exeter and Plymouth Gazette 18 September 1925 p 11 col 5
14   Western Times 2 October 1931 p 11

Bridge House, Bovey Tracey
1   Bovey Tracey Town Council web site 2013

Southbrook, Bovey Tracey
1   DHC – Bovey Tracey tithe map and apportionment
2   Western Times 10 May 1895 p 4 col 4;
     Exeter and Plymouth Gazette 21 May 1897 p 4 col 7
3   Exeter and Plymouth Gazette 25 June 1926 p 4 col 7; Western
     Times 21 July 1944 p 2 col 3
4   Visit by author, 26 May 2005

Beara, Bovey Tracey
1   Exeter Flying Post 8 June 1815 p 1 col 4
2   DHC – Bovey Tracey tithe map and apportionment
3   Visit by author, September 2000

Pullabrook, Bovey Tracey
1   DHC – Bovey Tracey tithe map, 1840
2   DHC – 1477M/L4-5
3   DHC – Bovey Tracey tithe map of 1840 and apportionment of
     1839 – item 1054, etc
4   www.britishlistedbuildings.co.uk

Plumley Farm, Bovey Tracey
1   English Heritage listing
2   Western Times 31 March 1876 p 1

Plumley Mine, Bovey Tracey
1   Exeter and Plymouth Gazette 17 May 1907 p 1 col 2; Atkinson
     et al, 1978, 42

Shaptor, Bovey Tracey
1   Atkinson et al, 1978, 43

Water, Manaton
1   Western Times 30 April 1886 p 1 col 1
2   Exeter and Plymouth Gazette 30 June 1905 p 1 col 6
3   Western Morning News 13 February 1999
4   Martin Watts, personal communication 1 September 2014

East Mill, Manaton
1   Baldwin, et al, 1999, 129
2   Manaton tithe apportionment 1842; Manaton census 1841,
     HO 107 254 bk 3 district 12 p 1; White, 1968; North Bovey
     census, 1861
3   Exeter Flying Post 14 January 1858 p 1 col 1
4   DHC – Manaton census 1861, RG9 1404 f 97 p 4; Manaton
     census 1871, RG10 2079 f 46 p 1
5   Western Times 11 September 1874 p 7 col 2
6   Western Times 5 June 1888 p 1 col 1; 3 July 1888 p 1 col 1; 14
     December 1888 p 4 col 1
7   Ordnance Survey map 1886; Manaton census 1901 – RG13
     2052: George Mortimore was resident, a carter on a farm
8   Manaton census 1891 – RG12 1697 f 83 p 1; Okehampton
     census 1901 – RG13 2124 f 45 p 31
9   Exeter and Plymouth Gazette 12 December 1919 p 4
10   Department of the Environment, List of Buildings of Special
     Architectural Interest. District of Teignbridge. Parishes of
     Manaton, Moretonhampstead and North Bovey, 1987, 26

Foxworthy Mill, Lustleigh
1   Elisabeth Stanbrook, 1987, 39
2   Lustleigh census 1841 – HO107 253/28;
     census 1851 – HO107 1871; Lydford census 1861 – RG 1458;
     Exeter Flying Post 12 August 1858 p 1 col 1
3   Elisabeth Stanbrook, 1987, 39
4   Visit on 27 April 1998 and talk with the then owner Geoff Morgan

Aller Mill, North Bovey
1   North Bovey census 1851 – HO107 1871 f 114 p 9; Western
     Times 1 September 1869 p 1
2   North Bovey census 1871 – RG10 2079; census 1881 –
     RG11 2160 f 66 p 1
3   Western Times 7 April 1903 p 6 col 2; Western Times 29 August
     1913 p 4 col 2; Exeter and Plymouth Gazette 15 April 1932 p 15

Blackaller Mill, North Bovey
1   DHC – D1508-1/T/D/2/2/1-4
2   Woolmer's Gazette 25 May 1839 p 2 col 1; see also Exeter
     Flying Post 7 October 1824 p 4 col 4
3   DHC – D1508-1/T/D/2/2/7
4   North Bovey census 1871 – RG10 2079

Great Wheal Eleanor, North Bovey
1   Hamilton Jenkin, 1974, 107-108; Exeter Flying Post 10 February
     1875 p 1 col 6; Western Times 4 February 1881 p 1 col 1

New Mill, North Bovey
1 Martin Watts, New Mill, North Bovey, Devon. A Report on the Mill for RW Architects. May 2005
2 Helen Harris, 1972, 210
3 North Bovey census, 1841 – HO107 253 bk 9 and HO107 253 bk 7 d 7 f 8 p 11
4 White's Directory, 1850; North Bovey census, 1851 – HO107 1871
5 North Bovey census, 1861 – RG9 1404 f 70 p 1; 1866 trade directory; Charles Aggett Torr, miller, Town Mills, Morris & Co's Commercial Directory and Gazetteer, 1870
6 Western Times 12 October 1883 p 1 col 2; 5 October 1884 p 4 col 1
7 Western Times 7 January 1887 p 1 col 1
8 Western Times 3 October 1895 p 2 col 1; Kelly's Directory of Devonshire 1902, 1065
9 Helen Harris, 1972, 210
10 English Heritage, Swindon – NMR ref SC00257
11 Martin Watts, personal communication 24 March 2007
12 Department of the Environment. List of Buildings of Special Architectural or Historic Interest. District of Teignbridge. Parishes of Manaton, Moretonhampstead and North Bovey, 1987, 183
13 Martin Watts, report 2005 (see above)

Bowden Mill. North Bovey
1 DHC – Z10/14/1a-b
2 Sherborne Mercury 3 July 1797 p 3; Exeter Flying Post 3 January 1799 p 3 col 4
3 Exeter Flying Post 18 September 1806 p 4; Sherborne Mercury 10 February 1812
4 North Bovey census 1841 – HO107/253/9 dist 8 f 4 p 2; census 1851 – HO107 1871 f 111 p 3; Western Times 26 July 1856 p 1 col 2
5 Morris & Co's Commercial Directory, 1870; Western Times 19 August 1881 p 4 col 2
6 Exeter and Plymouth Gazette 11 August 1882 p 6 col 3
7 Western Times 26 April 1886 p 4 col 2
8 Western Times 19 January 1891 p 2 col 1
9 Exeter and Plymouth Gazette 15 December 1891 p 1 col 2
10 Exeter and Plymouth Gazette 19 January 1892 p 1 col 2
11 Western Times 26 August 1892 p 6 col 4
12 Western Times 17 August 1894 p 5 col 1
13 Western Times 27 April 1900 p 4 col 2
14 North Bovey census 1901 – RG13 2052 f 54 p 3; Morchard Bishop census 1891 – RG12 1758; Moretonhampstead census 1911 – RG14 12720 sch 21
15 DHC – 5016B/MT10; English Heritage Swindon NMR ref SC00257

16 Department of the Environment. List of Buildings of Special Architectural or Historic Interest. District of Teignbridge. Parishes of Manaton, Moretonhampstead and North Bovey, 1987, 141; visit by author in 2000; information from Tom Greeves 9 September 2014
17 Western Renewable Energy web site

Gratnar Tin Mill, North Bovey
1 Tom Greeves, Blowing and Knocking. The Dartmoor Tin Mill before 1750. Dartmoor Magazine, 23, Summer 1991, 18-20

West Coombe, North Bovey
1 Visit by author 23 March 1997
2 DHC – 4930 B/T/B/21 & 22
3 DHC – 4930 B/T/B/23 and 24
4 Western Times 13 October 1882 p 1 col 3

East Vitifer Mine, North Bovey
1 Harris, 1992, 210
2 Harris, op cit; Western Times 13 October 1882 p 1 col 3 [watercourse at West Coombe]
3 DHC – 4930 B/L/1; North Bovey census 1851 – HO107 1871 f114 p9

West Mill, Manaton
1 DHC - 924B/E1/9
2 Greeves, T. A. P., Tinworking at Heathercombe, Manaton, (unpublished) 1991. Via Heritage Gateway
3 Baldwin, et al, 1999, 87, 89
4 Greeves, T. A. P., 1991, op cit
5 DHC – 924B/E1/9
6 Western Times 12 March 1831 p 1 col 1
7 DHC – Manaton tithe apportionment 1842
8 Pike, 1993, 31

Vogwell Farm, Manaton
1 Pike, 1993, 63; personal communication from Derek Greenaway 11 October 2014
2 Baldwin, et al, 1999, 73
3 Manaton census 1901 – RG13 2052
4 Western Times 19 November 1912 p 4 col 2

Heatree, Manaton
1 Ordnance Survey map, 1st edition, 25in, 1886; Baldwin et al, 1999, 88-90
2 Site visit by author 2 October 2014; Exeter and Plymouth Gazette 23 October 1903 p 5 col 1
3 Ordnance Survey map, 1: 2,500, 1905

4   Ordnance Survey map, 1:2,500, 1958
5   Obituary, Western Times 31 January 1947
6   Western Morning News, 20 September 1944

Batworthy Mills, Chagford
1   Sherborne Mercury 7 March 1785
2   Sherborne Mercury 17 June 1805
3   Exeter Flying Post 6 September 1855 p 8 col 3;
    Chagford census 1851, Mill Street – HO107 1885 f 509 p 7
4   Chagford census 1851, HO107 1885 f 560 p 3; Western Times
    27 June 1857 p 4 col 1; Western Times 10 October 1857
    p 5 col 2
5   Exeter Flying Post 27 June 1866 p 1 col 3
6   Western Times 1 March 1872 p 1 col 2
7   Western Times 17 July 1868 p 7
8   Western Times 3 August 1877 p 4 col 3
9   Chagford census 1881 – RG11 2225
10 Kelly's Directory of Devonshire 1908, 1088-1090; Western
    Times 20 August 1915 p 8 col 4
11 English Heritage listing 94533

Lingcombe tinners mill, Chagford
1   Personal communication, Tom Greeves 20 August 2014

New Vitifer Mine, Chagford
1   Mike Passmore, DTRG Newsletter 32, January 2007, 4
2   Exeter Flying Post 14 July 1875 p 1 col 2

Smithy Park tinners mill, Lustleigh
1   Tom Greeves, Tinners and Tinworks of the Bovey Tracey area
    from Prehistory to the Twentieth Century. Trans. Devonshire
    Association, 140, December 2008, 27-28

Lustleigh Mill, Lustleigh
1   Crowdy, ed., 2001, 81
2   Martin Watts, 2002, 120
3   Crowdy, ed., 2001, 81
4   SHC, Taunton – DD/WY/47/3/49 – for 1718
5   Crowdy, ed., 2001, 81
6   Lustleigh tithe apportionment 1837; White's Devonshire
    Directory 1850; Lustleigh census for 1841 and 1851
7   Western Times 3 December 1875 p 1 col 1
8   Exeter Flying Post 10 May 1876 p 1 col 2; Western Times 26
    May 1876 p 5 col 1
9   Crowdy, ed., 2001; White's Directory 1878
10 Western Times 9 March 1888 p 1 col 4
11 Crowdy, ed., 2001

12 Western Times 13 January 1893 p 1 col 1; Western Times 27
    November 1893 p 1 col 1
13 Crowdy, ed., 2001

Casely tin blowing mill, Lustleigh
1   Dr Tom Greeves, Tinners and Tinworks of the Bovey Tracey
    area from Prehistory to the Twentieth Century, Trans.
    Devonshire Association, 140, December 2008, 28, citing: DHC
    1837Z/add.Z7

Kelly Mine, Bovey Tracey
1   Kelly Mine Preservation Society web site; Allen et al, 2014,
    14-15
2   Atkinson et al, 1978, 38
3   Visit by author 29 May 2004; Brooks, 2004, 156
4   Nick Walter, Kelly Mine Open Day, Dartmoor Tinworkers
    Research Group Newsletter 19, July 2000, 2

East Wrey, Lustleigh
1   Western Times 6 November 1914 p 4 col 4
2   Dr T. A. Greeves, 23 July 1985 quoted in Devon C.C. Sites and
    Monuments Register 20/08/85.

Steward Mill, Moretonhampstead
1   Sherborne Mercury c19 August 1811
2   Exeter Flying Post 29 June 1826 p 1 col 4
3   Martin Bodman, Tanning in Devon in the Nineteenth Century,
    Trans. Devonshire Association, vol. 141, 2009, 219-236;
    Bodman, 2008, 91-92
4   Western Times 23 April 1836 p 2 col 3
5   Western Times 10 March 1849 p 1 col 1; White's Devon, 1850,
    reprinted New York 1968, 478
6   Moretonhampstead census 1851, HO107 1871
7   Exeter Flying Post 19 December 1860 p 1 col 1
8   Moretonhampstead census 1861 – RG12 1669 f 44 p18; census
    1871 – RG10 2078
9   Harrod's Directory, Devonshire, 1878; Kelly's Directory of
    Devonshire 1908, 1088-1090
10 DHC – 5016B/MT11 of 1911; English Heritage, Swindon, NMR
    ref SC00257
11 Visit by author, November 1998

One Mill, Moretonhampstead
1   Silvester Treleaven, Chronological Occurrences in
    Moretonhampstead, (1799-1830), transcribed by T. N. H. Neck,
    1924 – Moretonhampstead History Society
2   DHC – Moretonhampstead tithe apportionment, 1839

3   Exeter Flying Post 27 November 1867 p 1 col 3
4   St John Thomas, 1960, 58

Millbrook Mill, Moretonhampstead
1   Moretonhampstead History Society web site
2   Friend, 1994, 27 and 74
3   Western Times 4 July 1865 p 2 col 5
4   Advice from Martin Watts 4 October 2014
5   Moretonhampstead census 1871 – RG10 2078 f 32 p 12; census
     1881 – RG11 2160 f 38 p 14

Coombe Farm, Moretonhampstead
1   Department of the Environment. List of Buildings of Special
     Architectural or Historic Interest. District of Teignbridge.
     Parishes of Manaton, Moretonhampstead and North Bovey,
     1987, 53
2   Western Times 26 July 1872 p 1 col 3
3   As item 1, from notes by T. Greeves, 1985
4   English Heritage, Swindon NMR ref SC00257

Liverton Brook

Stover Lodge Farm, Teigngrace
1   Royal Exchange Fire Insurance Policy 204570, 19 November
     1803
2   Woolmer's Gazette 24 March 1827 p 1 col 3

Lurcombe, Bickington
1   Western Times 30 July 1909 p 4 col 4

Liverton Mill, Ilsington
1   Sherborne Mercury 4 February 1771
2   Royal Exchange Fire Insurance Policy 2032808, October 1803
3   Royal Exchange Fire Insurance Policy 212398, 22 December
     1804
4   DHC – Ilsington tithe map and apportionment, 1838, item 719
5   White's Directory of Devonshire 1850; Exeter Flying Post
     26 November 1857 p 1 col 3
6   Trade directories, including Harrods Directory, 1878
7   Ilsington census 1871 – RG10 2081 f 57 p 7
8   Western Times 28 September 1886 p 3 col 2
9   Western Times 20 September 1890 p 1 col 2
10   Martin Watts, report to owners, 2008
11   Dr Tom Greeves, Tinners and Tinworks of the Bovey Tracey
     area from Prehistory to the Twentieth Century. Trans.
     Devonshire Association, 140, December 2008, 30-31

Manganese mine, Pool estate, Ilsington
1   DHC – 924B/L46/6 of 1814
2   Ilsington tithe map and apportionment (1838)

Silver Brook Mine, Ilsington
1   P. Newman, English Heritage – Archaeological Field
     Investigation Report 30 August 2005; Exeter Flying Post 17
     June 1852 p 4 col 3
2   Western Times 2 April 1853 p 7 col 4
3   Exeter and Plymouth Gazette 25 October 1856 p 8 col 5;
     Western Times 9 May 1857 p 6 col 5
4   Exeter Flying Post 26 November 1857 p 5 col 6; Newman P.,
     op cit, 2005

Atlas and Smallacombe Mine, Ilsington
1   Dr Tom Greeves, Tinners and Tinworks of the Bovey Tracey
     area from Prehistory to the Twentieth Century. Trans.
     Devonshire Association, 140, December 2008, 33-35; Hamilton
     Jenkin, 2005, 128 - 127
2   English Heritage, cited in
     www.legendarydartmoor.co.uk/atlas_burn.htm
3   Hamilton Jenkin, 2005, 129, citing Mining Journal 22 July and
     23 October 1859, 21 April and 8 September 1860
4   Exeter and Plymouth Gazette 20 November 1863 p 4 col 5; 25
     November 1863 p 1 col 2; Bristol Mercury 26 December
     1863 (mentions 60ft waterwheel)
5   Hamilton Jenkin, 2005, 128-129; Exeter and Plymouth Gazette 5
     December 1873 p 3 cols 6 and 7
6   DHC – 58/8/3/2 and 58/8/3/5
7   DHC – 58/8/3/3 of 1872
8   The Times, 1 May 1873
9   Burt et al. 1984, 3-4
10   Tom Greeves, Historic Mining Image No 2. Burning House at
     Atlas Tin Mine, Ilsington, with launder leading to stamps
     waterwheel, c 1900. DTRG Newsletter 39, July 2010, 16-17
11   Exeter and Plymouth Gazette 11 November 1910 p 1 col 6
12   Ransom, 2005, 67-68

Bibliography

Adams, Brian, *Bovey Tracey Potteries 1750-1836*, B. & T. Thorn, Budleigh Salterton, 1993

Adams, Brian and Thomas, Anthony, *A potwork in Devonshire: the history and products of the Bovey Tracey potteries 1750-1836*, Bovey Tracey, Sayce Publishing, 1996

Adams, Brian, *Bovey Tracey Potteries. Guide and Marks,* House of Marbles, Bovey Tracey, 2005

Allen, D. W., et al, *Kelly Mine. And Introductory Guide to the Site and its Equipment*, Kelly Mine Preservation Society, 2014

Atkinson, Michael, with Roger Burt and Peter Waite, *Dartmoor Mines. The Mines of the Granite Mass*, Exeter Industrial Archaeology Group, University of Exeter, 1978

Baldwin, Jean, et al, *The Book of Manaton, Portrait of a Dartmoor Parish*, Halsgrove, 1999

Beavis, Derek, Newton Abbot. *The Story of the Town's Past,* Barracuda Books, Buckingham, 1985

Beresford, M. W. and Finberg, H. P. R., *English Medieval Boroughs, A Hand-list.* David & Charles, 1973

Bliss, Jane, et al, editors, *Aspects of Devon History. People, Places and Landscapes*, Devon History Society, 2012

Bodman, Martin, *Devon Leather*, Leat Press, 2008

Bond, Jack, *Dunsford Memories*, c 1997

Bone, Mile and Stanier, Peter, *A Guide to the Industrial Archaeology of Devon*, Association for Industrial Archaeology, 1998

Brooks, Tony, *Great Rock. Devon's Last 'Metal' Mine*, Cornish Hillside Publications, 2004

Burt, Roger, Waite, Peter, Burnley, Ray, *Devon and Somerset Mines. Metalliferous and Associated Minerals, 1845-1913*, University of Exeter, 1984

Chudleigh History Group, *The Chudleigh Book*, Orchard Publications, 2009

Collins, J. H., *Observations on the West of England Mining Region, Plymouth*, 1912, 507

Crossing, William, *The Teign from Moor to Sea*, Quay Books, 1986

Crowdy, Joe, ed., *The Book of Lustleigh. Portrait of a Dartmoor Parish*, Halsgrove, 2001

Earle, John, Dartmoor. *Walks into History*, Halsgrove, 2003

Edwards, Richard A., *Devon's Non-Metal Mines*, Halsgrove, 2011

Foreman, Wilfred, *Oxfordshire Mills*, Phillmore, 1983

Fraser, Iain, *The Palk Family. Haldon House & Torquay*, Sylverwood Publishing, 2008

Friend, George, *Memories of Moretonhampstead*

Gifford, Alan, *Derbyshire Watermills. Corn Mills*, Midland Wind & Water Mills Group, 1999

Gill, Crispin, ed., *Dartmoor. A New Study*, David & Charles, 1970

Gray, Todd, ed., *Travels in Georgian Devon. The Illustrated Journals of the Reverend John Swete (1789-1900), Volume II*, Halsgrove, 1998

Gray, Todd, *Dartmoor Engraved*, Mint Press, 2001

Greeves, Tom & Newman, Phil, *The Great Courts of Devon Tinners 1510 and 1710,* Dartmoor Tinworking Research Group, 2011

Hall, Tim, *From Haldon to Mid-Dartmoor in Old Photographs*, Alan Sutton, Stroud, 1990

Hamilton Jenkin, A. K., *Mines of Devon*, Devon Books, Landmark Publishing, 2005

Hamilton Leggett, Peter, *The Dartmoor Bibliography*, Devon Books, 1992

Harris, Helen, *The Industrial Archaeology of Dartmoor*, Peninsula Press, 1992

Hayter-Hames, Jane, *History of Chagford*, Rushford, 2004; also 1981 edition, Phillimore

Healey, Sherryl, *The Parke Estate*, Bovey Tracey Heritage Trust, c 2000 (leaflet)

Hemery, Eric, *Walking the Dartmoor Waterways*, Peninsula Press, 1991

Hoskins, W. G., *Devon*, Devon Books, 1992

Lander, Reg, *Mining. Yarner Copper Mine*, Bovey Tracey Heritage Trust, 2012 (leaflet)

Moore, Rev. T., *The History of Devonshire from the Earliest Period to the Present*, London, 1829

Newman, Phil, *The Dartmoor Tin Industry, A Field Guide*, Chercombe Press, 1998

Paget, Michael, ed., *Throwleigh. Pictures and memories from a Dartmoor parish,* The Throwleigh Archive, 2006

Pike, Claude, *Heathercombe, The History of a Dartmoor Valley*, West Country Books, 1993

Radford, Roy and Ursula, *The Book of South Tawton and South Zeal,* Halsgrove, 2000

Rice, I., 2002 *The Book of Chagford*, Halsgrove Publishing

Richardson, P. H. G., *Mines of Dartmoor and the Tamar Valley*, Devon Books, 1995

Rippon, Stephen, Claughton, Peter, and Smart, Chris, *Mining in a Medieval Landscape. The Royal Silver Mines of the Tamar Valley*, University of Exeter Press, 2009

Robins, John, *Follow the Leat*, privately published, 1984

Rolt, L. T. C., *The Potter's Field. History of the South Devon Ball Clay Industry*, David & Charles, 1971

St John Thomas, David, *A Regional History of the Railways of Great Britain. Volume 1. The West Country*, Phoenix House, 1960

Schmitz, C. J., *The Teign Valley Lead Mines*, Northern Cavern and Mine Research Society, Sheffield, 1973

Schmitz, C. J., *The Teign Valley Silver-Lead Mines 1806-1880*, Northern Mine Research Society monograph, 1980

Stanbrook, Elisabeth, *Dartmoor. Pictures from the Past,* Quay Publications, Brixham, 1987

Surridge, F. W., *The Finest of the Wheat from Bridford Mills, Devon*, 1950

Tregoning, Lance, *Bovey Tracey. An Ancient Town. Its Story and Legend*, Bovey Tracey: Cottage Publishing, 1983

Tregoning, Lance, *Bovey Tracey in Bygone Days. A Portrait of a Dartmoor Town*, Devon Books, 1989

Varwell, Emmie, *Throwleigh, The Story of a Dartmoor Village*, Sydney Lee, 1938

Wade Martins, Susanna, *The English Model Farm. Building the Agricultural Ideal, 1700-1914,* Windgather Press, 2002

Waterfield, R., *Parochial History of Bridford*, c 1939

Watts, Martin, *The Archaeology of Mills and Milling*, Tempus, 2002

Watts, Martin, *Corn Milling*, Shire Library, 2008

White, William, *White's Devon, 1850*, reprinted New York, 1968

Wills, Dick, *The Book of Ilsington, A Photographic History of the Parish*, Halsgrove, 2000

Woodward-Nutt, Jim, ed., *Mills Open*, Mills Section, The Society for the Preservation of Ancient Buildings, 2007

Worth, R.Hansford, *Dartmoor,* The Author's Executors, Plymouth, 1953 (Republished with a new introduction by G. M. Spooner, David and Charles, Newton Abbot, 1967)

Index

A

I

Ideford
 Coombe Mill   122
 Ideford Mill   122
 Oldchard water pump   122
Ilsington
 Atlas and Smallacombe Mines   115
 burning house   115
 Bagtor House   118
 Bagtor Mill   118
 Crownley Parks   118
 Ingsdon Mill   118
 Liverton Mills   113
 Lower Sigford   118
 Middlecott Pond   116
 Middlecott Wood   116
 Sigford Consols   118
 Silver Brook Mine   115
 Smallacombe farm   116
 Smallacombe Mine   116
 Smith's Wood mine   118
 Wheal Lemon   118
Ingsdon Mill, Ilsington   118
Ipplepen
 Bickley Mill   121
 Lower Bickley Mill   121
Iron Mills, Dunsford   47
Ironfounders   10
 Bartle   11, 33, 109
 Beare, Henry   11, 98, 111
 Bodley Bros   11, 75
 Bodley, W. C.   48, 98
 Dingey, Francis   32
 Harris, G. H.   11, 65
 Harvey & Co   33, 34
 Mare, J. E.   33
 Martin & Parkin   11
 Mathews   29
 Perran Foundry   33
 Plymouth Foundry   33
 Polyblank   11, 69
 Stenner & Gunn   11, 35, 36
 Taylor and Bodley   11
 Webber   11

Willcocks   11, 107
 Willmit   107
Ironmongers
 Helson, John   48
 Walker, W.   34

J

Jackson, William   92
James, Henry   29, 45
Jevons, Carrel   80
Jewsbridge Mill, Teigngrace   83
Johnson, Percy   40

K

Kelly Mine, Bovey Tracey   107
Kelly Mine Preservation Society   107
Keyberry Mill, Newton Abbot   121
Kilmer, William   96
Kingskerswell
 Kingskerswell Mill   121
 Tannery   121
Kingsteignton
 Abbrook pump   122
 Bellamarsh Mills   16
 Higher Mill   122
 Lower Mill   122
 Sandygate Mill   122
 Town Mill   122
Kingswear   116
Kitson, John   102
Knapman family   59, 74
Knapman, H.   39
Knapman, J. A.   74
Knapman, William   74, 77
Knight, Robert   21
Knowling, Richard   115

L

Lanacraft, William   97
Landowners   10
 Clifford   10, 16, 18, 20
 Commercial Union   44
 Cornwall, Duchy of   68

Devon, Earls of   10, 51, 52, 53, 56,
  96
 Drewe family   56
 Ellis, William   59
 Exmouth, Lord   10, 32, 34, 35
 Foxford, Robert   95
 Fulford   10, 45, 46, 47
 Fulton, Edward Arthur Craig   56
 Hambleden, Lord   10, 51, 56, 98,
  100, 111
 Hellyer, Christopher   26
 Hole, William   91, 92
 Hole, William R.   91
 Kitson, Rev. John   102
 Lyon, Alfred   116
 National Trust   54
 Palk   10, 28, 31, 32, 36, 43, 44, 45
 Somerset, Duke of   88, 112
 Templer, George   88
 Templer, James   112
 Templer, Lord   16
 Widger, Thomas   114
Lane, Thomas   80
Langdon, William   39
Langworthy, Lewis   35
Latimer, Lord   96
Leach, William   28
Leats
 Bovey Pottery   85, 87, 88
 Bradford Tinwork   72, 77
 Frog Mill, Throwleigh   74
Gidleigh Mill   72
 Holwell Tor Water   88
 Lower Smithy Park, Lustleigh   105
 New Mill, North Bovey   97
 South Zeal   78
 Southill, Chagford   70
 Tawton Mill   80
 Vitifer   70
 Zeal Leat   78
Leats and weirs   8
Lee, William Henry   90
Lemonford Mill, Bickington   118
Lewis, John   94, 97
Lewis, William   66
Lignite   84

146

Whiteway, Bessie 24
Whiteway, John 18, 23, 24
Whiteway, Walter 24
Whiteway, William 24
Widdicombe, Joseph 23
Widger, Thomas 114
Wilde, Arthur 56
Willcocks of Buckfastleigh 11, 107
Williams, John 43
Williams, Richard 79
Williams, William 27
Willmit, William 107, 108
Wills, Charles Corbyn 113, 115
Wills, George 113
Wills, Sir Chaning 27

Wills, Thomas 32
Wise, John 29
Wonson Mill, Throwleigh 74
Wood, Robert 21
Woollen manufacturers
    Berry, John 62
    Berry, Richard 62, 64
    Vicary, Fulford 62
    White, Mr 110
Worth, W. H. 61, 66, 68
Wotton, Daniel 20
Wotton, John 20, 22
Wotton, William 20
Wray Brook 106, 108, 111
Wrayford, Ann 50

Wyatt, Albert John 90
Wyatt, Charles Leslie 90
Wyatt, Edward 89, 90
Wyndhurst, Throwleigh 74

Y

Yarner Copper Mine, Bovey Tracey 88
Yarner Wood 87
Yeo Mill, Chagford 69

Z

Zeal Mill, South Tawton 76, 79

A Teign mill in 1835 'Bridford Mill' by W. Traies. But is it? It is not Bridford Mill on the Teign and it does not appear to fit the topography at Stone Mill. Has Traies created an imaginary landscape or did this mill exist? A remote possibility is the Barytes Mine at Bridford, where the site of a ruined mill was noted in later years. *Painting courtesy of the Royal Albert Memorial Museum, Exeter*

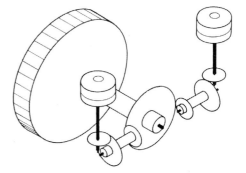

Weir Mill, Drewsteignton

Top: painting by John Wallace Tucker (1808-1869). Today there is evidence of a by-pass channel to the left of the low-breastshot waterwheel, which was about 12ft by 22in. There was also a second waterwheel at the other end of the building, possibly driving a single pair of stones. *Private collection.*

Left and centre: remains of treble gearing with face and lantern gears, photographed in 1941.
Donald W. Muggeridge/Martin Watts collection.

Right: a treble gearing layout, with drives to two pairs of stones, which may have existed at Weir Mill, powered by the waterwheel seen in the painting. *Drawing by Martin Watts*

There is another painting, by Reverend Swete, made in March 1794, of 'Clifford Mill' which is almost certainly of Weir Mill, with a thatched roof. The mill was rebuilt with a slate roof after a conflagration in 1833, thought to have been caused by arson. See also pages 51 and 52